Longing for Recognition

The Joys, Complexities, and Contradictions of
Practicing Dietetics

by Jacqueline Rochelle Gingras, PhD

RAW
NERVE
BOOKS

Longing for Recognition:
The Joys, Complexities, and Contradictions of Practicing Dietetics
Copyright © Jacqueline Rochelle Gingras
First published in 2009 by:
Raw Nerve Books
Centre for Women's Studies
University of York
York YO10 5DD
England
www.rawnervebooks.co.uk

British Library-in-publication Data.
A catalogue record for this book is available from the British Library.
ISBN: 978-0-9553586-5-4

Cover and book design by Hilary Kay Doran

Printed and bound by:
MPG Biddles Ltd,
24 Rollesby Road, Hardwick Industrial Estate
King's Lynn, Norfolk
PE30 4LS
UK

To the uprising of students
who have the courage to write of their lives.

Acknowlegments

There are many people I wish to acknowledge for their contributions and support in enabling this book to be made possible. Foremost, my sister dietitians for sharing ardent expressions of your work, for leaping into conversations so willingly, and for telling stories of your life through which I came to learn of myself...thank you. Our time together was truly a gift.

Gwen Chapman, Karen Meyer, and Cynthia Nicol, my virtuous and intrepid dissertation committee members, I offer my thanks to you for inspiring me with your own stories, for sharing your thoughtful responses to my writing, and for questioning me on what it was I intended to accomplish with this book – until I felt convinced of it myself. It has been my special privilege to work with you. My thanks for shepherding this story through the academy.

My thanks to the Killam Memorial Trust, Social Sciences and Humanities Research Council, and the Faculty of Community Services at Ryerson University for contributing financial support during the writing and publishing of this work.

And Lucy Aphramor, my chthonic thirteenth participant, a heartfelt thanks for sharing your poetic gifts and your charming ways of disrupting dietetic practice. You inspire me to believe that dietetics can be more just, just more. I look forward to continuing to find words together that spell out such possibilities.

My deepest gratitude to Raw Nerve Books, Ann Kaloski Naylor, and Hilary Doran for daring to embrace this story and showing the text (and the author) such thoughtful care and attention through the publishing process.

My family, you deserve an extraordinary tribute for embracing my academic and artistic inclinations no matter how far flung. I love and appreciate all of you for co-creating these stories of our lives. My children, Evyn and Lewis for filling me with wonder and setting for me a tremendous challenge of becoming. And finally, to my partner Kelly. The words to craft this story have been found only because you afforded me the time and space to write. Over the years, you selflessly gift me these things and more and I am forever grateful as I continually marvel at your strength, courage, intelligence, and grace. All my love and gratitude to you.

Table of Contents

Introduction

In *Longing for Recognition* I endeavour to enact autoethnography, to bring it alive through a storying called autofiction. Although some characters stem entirely from my imagination, most are based on and inspired by my research co-participants, my academic colleagues, my friends, and my family. Most of these people are provided with pseudonyms to protect their identity and preserve their anonymity; a few retain their given names. Those whose real names are used have read the excerpts in which they appear and have agreed to be represented as such. I endeavour to show these characters 'embedded in the complexities of lived moments of struggle...attempting to preserve or restore the continuity and coherence of life's unity in the face of unexpected blows of fate that call one's meanings and values into question' (Ellis & Bochner, 2000, p. 744). I've recreated characters' lives by making choices about dialogue, language, imagery, metaphor, narration, and conflict to illustrate implicitly the research themes. Each chapter is set initially in Tess's classroom. The twelve chapters following the prologue correspond to the twelve lessons of an imaginary dietetic course, 'NUTRITION 430: Orientations to Dietetic Practice,' offered over the span of a fall semester. A course outline and glossary are provided as supporting documents. After each class, scenes shift to a variety of locations. I offer this book as the centrepiece from which an imaginary of dietetic education and practice might emerge. I hope it will inspire readers to ask, 'What if this were true? What then?'

The impulse for this work arose from my desire to understand the connections between what I know as dietetic education and the complex world in which it is situated and constituted. From the start, I was concerned with discovering ways to represent this research unconventionally. I searched 'for alternative ways to push and move the already constituted towards new discursive practices' (Søndergaard, 2005, p. 298). During the research process,

I learned of myself through the Other. I engaged with the Other, assured that relationships form the crucible of my learning. My actions are premised on reciprocity, mutuality, and respect. Most of all, any knowing I claim exists in the dynamic embeddedness of these relationships. I believe that this research, like all pieces of writing, is a work of translation in the way Hrjinian (2000) describes translation as an epistemological project that 'scrutinizes the nature of knowing and the way in which any particular knowing is circumstantially embedded' (p. 296). It is my hope that my translation provokes further dialogue on the subject of dietetic education and practice. It is my hope that this work provokes dialogue that places the subject of dietetic education and practice in translation and leaves it there unsettled, leaves it there unkept.

Prologue

All seeing is hooded with loss …
in looking at the other … the subject seeks to see herself.
(Phelan, 1993, p. 16)

Jacqui and her grandmother sat side by side in two oversized recliners watching *The Wheel of Fortune – The Wheel,* as her family called it, with affectionate familiarity. At seven o'clock, when *The Wheel* was on, Grandma was not to be disturbed. Despite knowing this, Jacqui could not wait to share her big news.

'Grandma?' Jacqui paused, her heart beating wildly. A hard swallow. 'I'm pregnant.' Jacqui's throat was dry with nervousness. She didn't take her eyes off Pat and Vanna.

Grandma leaned forward in her recliner, her head turned towards Jacqui. Her crocheting fell into her lap. 'Oh, Jacqui … what, how did this happen?' It didn't take much imagination to guess Grandma was not thrilled by the announcement – and its ramifications.

'Well, Kelly and I chose a donor and I was inseminated about two months ago. It worked the first time.' Jacqui tried to evoke a celebratory tone, but the words shrivelled on her parched tongue.

'Oh, my goodness. What did your mother say?' Grandma got right to the point.

'She was pretty surprised. I think Dad was excited, though.' Jacqui began to feel queasy.

'That's OK, dear. It'll be alright. Everything will work out. This was meant to be and God loves all children. Don't ever forget that.'

'I'm sure he does, Grandma. I'm sure he does.' Jacqui stared at the TV. In her head she thought, 'I'd like to solve the puzzle, Pat.'

ès·

Jacqui remembered exactly when she finally decided she wanted to have a baby. It was the moment she first held her newborn nephew in her arms. September 3, 2002. When he started to cry, something in her heart cracked, melted, and spilled into her body. She found herself utterly surprised by her response. Who was this little boy who moved her so deeply, this little baby whose cry instantaneously pierced her rigid armour? He was only his tiny, fragile self. Jacqui watched wide-eyed as his mother gently took him from her and held him close to ease his crying. Jacqui had no choice but to let the astonished tears cascade down her face. There was no hiding the force with which baby Luke captured her spirit and her imagination, and planted the belief that maybe she, too, could be a mother.

Less than one year later, Jacqui and her partner, Kelly, had decided on an anonymous donor, subjected themselves to physical and emotional tests for parental suitability, and gone forward with the first insemination. They had purchased enough sperm for six tries. One was all they needed. Even knowing all their painstaking arrangements, Jacqui was surprised when she saw the pregnancy test was positive. It was completely surreal. The first couple of months passed by uneventfully, but then morning sickness hit, sucking Jacqui into a fog-like distress. Oranges, grapefruit, and popsicles were virtually all she could eat. The progress on her doctoral research ground to a frustrating halt. As her body grew rounder and more awkward, she began to absorb the reality of their changing lives. Kelly, meanwhile, had already started buying the smallest baby outfits imaginable and searching for a midwife. Together they were learning to become parents.

It came time to share the joyful news with Jacqui's parents, but Jacqui wondered if they would think it joyful?

Jacqui's mother, who had just gotten over the shock of her daughter's coming out four years earlier, responded, 'Well, you're determined to pull me into the twenty-first century, aren't you?'

At a visit to their therapist soon after, Jacqui and Kelly were reassured that when the baby arrived, all the current disappointments, turmoil, and grieving would be forgotten. 'Babies have a way of pulling people into the present moment,' she said. 'Trust me.' Mercifully, she was right.

Evyn's birth was a wondrous miracle. Jacqui's sister, Suzanne, worked with Kelly throughout the long labour, trying to soothe and encourage Jacqui, whose groans and complaints continued right up to the moment of birth. Her parents were transfixed as they held her in their arms. Perfect baby. Perfect joy. Photos capture forever the sheer joy and relief in their smiles. Suzanne was named Evyn's guardian. When the grandparents and great-grandparents finally met Evyn, there was no mention of their original apprehension and disapproval, no sign of it anywhere on their faces, just pure happiness. The therapist had been right. All of their agony about this child being born into a same-sex parent family seemed to vanish. But Jacqui remembered. Even though she moved past her naïve excitement with which she announced the pregnancy to her family, she carried their initial response in her cells, in her heart's memory. She knew her life was different than that of a straight parent, yet she still wanted to show the world that she had a place in it.

Maybe that need to prove herself explained her desire for a doctorate. 'Life,' she told her mother, 'there's no master plan. I just follow my passion.' She knew that was not as disciplined as her mother would have wanted despite her life's accomplishments. She tried not to let that bother her. She never stopped trying.

Jacqui and Kelly's community of friends, gay and straight, welcomed Evyn's birth announcement with ardent joy. Love and congratulations rushed in from all around them. Jacqui's close friend Tess was one of the first to meet Evyn after she arrived home from the hospital. Tess and her daughter, Zoë, had phoned shortly after the baby had arrived home, asking if they could come over for the briefest of visits. Nine-year-old Zoë was smitten, gingerly offering her finger for Evyn to grasp as Tess cradled her close. 'She's so delicate. Look how she puts her thumb between her two fingers. Cool. My teacher says that's a sign of shyness.' So many signs baby Evyn was showing the world. As her world asked, 'Who are you?', she responded.

'Evyn Shona Stalker-Gingras.' Jacqui practised the name, her voice brimming with pride but still beset by bewilderment. Watching Kelly and Evyn start a tradition of slow dancing to George Michael before bed, Jacqui wondered to herself, 'Is this our child? How did this happen?' Soon after Evyn was born, Jacqui found poetry writing its way through her.

> *One look...*
> *we are ploughed under by it.*
> *Our love for you*
> *brings us to fall on our knees.*
> *Tears of joy*
> *catch wet in our throats.*
> *We are startled by*
> *our love for you.*
>
> *Your presence ...*
> *pulls us more fully into life.*
> *We stumble, staggered by salted currents*
> *motioning the sand beneath our feet.*
> *Hot waves of maternal desire*
> *rise up, blushing our cheeks.*
> *We are overcome.*
> *We are undone by*
> *our love for you.*

One turn ...
a caress, longing, familiar
sweet baby girl
you unlock a dark, mystic chamber
long nameless in our hearts.
Your mothers gaze through lavender mists,
waking dreams, tenderly, wanton.
You beckon us into the swirl of natality with
our love for you.

After three blissful months of mothers and baby luxuriating in the process of getting to know each other and travelling across Canada to introduce Evyn to Kelly's family, Jacqui returned to her research. She managed to pull together a submission for the ethics review board and finalize plans for interviews and workshops while Evyn napped. Much was accomplished during those interludes. Evyn would be rocking in her swing, Sarah McLachlan's *Afterglow* soothing her to sleep, while Jacqui typed away on the computer. Jacqui wondered if Evyn would be forever bound to associate the tap-tap of a computer keyboard with a peaceful nap.

A few months into the New Year, Dr Alice Taylor, a nutrition professor at the university where Jacqui was doing her research, emailed her and asked if she would be interested in teaching an undergraduate course. 'Your supervisor put your name forward since you are doing research on dietetic education. Are you available? The course starts in the fall. I've just been granted a research leave and need to find a replacement instructor. It is only two credits. A two-hour class, once a week. Tuesdays.' Alice's request carried a note of urgency.

Jacqui hesitated. She was just entering the data collection and analysis phase of her research and didn't have much extra time to plan a course. Kelly was also working hard to finish her degree, and, of course, there was Evyn to care for as well. Jacqui had hoped she would be writing in the fall. Yet, she was eager to teach. She loved teaching. And to put some of her pedagogical and curricular theory into practice in the dietetic classroom would be exciting. 'How much time would be involved in planning the course?' Jacqui asked.

'It's already planned. There is a text, course outline, syllabus. It's done. I've taught it for seven years, so there is nothing you need to do but step into the classroom.'

'OK. Could you send me the course materials by email and I'll have a look and get back to you by the end of the week with a decision either way.' Jacqui felt uneasy not telling Alice of her other obligations, but she needed to be sure of whether she would want to teach the course before making a final decision.

'Great. Wonderful!' Alice's enthusiasm made it seem like Jacqui had already agreed to take over the course.

When Jacqui looked at the course outline and syllabus, her heart sank. Much of what was expected of the students enrolled in NUTRITION 430: Orientations to Dietetic Practice, was to prepare and deliver a PowerPoint presentation based on theories underlying effective communication. There was nothing about critical social theory, feminism, or sociology – all what Jacqui believed to be fundamental elements of students' orientation to dietetic practice. If she were to agree to teach the course, Jacqui would have to modify the entire syllabus, and that just wasn't possible given her research and parental commitments. She regretted the timing, but it was an opportunity she would have to let pass.

Before she called Alice to let her know her decision, she phoned Tess. There was no answer on Tess's office phone, so she left a message. 'Hi, Tess. It's me. I just got a call from a prof in nutrition who needs a sessional for a course this fall. I really wish I could do it, but I just don't have the time. Baby, job, PhD! You know how it is! Anyway, would you be interested? Call me.'

Tess was definitely interested, although her life was extremely full, too. Tess had completed her masters in adult education over five years ago and, although she was an occasional guest speaker in the classroom, she wanted to bring her knowledge into the dietetics classroom in a more systematic way: she wanted to teach a course of her own. Before discussing the situation with Jacqui, Tess talked with her clinical supervisor, asking if it would be possible to start after lunch on Tuesdays and work later to accommodate her teaching shedule. Despite knowing she would be overloaded for the duration of the term, Tess felt this opportunity was not to be missed, and she shared her enthusiasm with Jacqui by phone the next day. Jacqui then got in touch with Alice to express her dismay for having to turn down the teaching opportunity and to suggest her colleague, Tess, instead. Alice was expecting Tess's call when it came later that week.

'Hello Dr. Taylor.' Tess was surprised to find herself more than a little nervous.

'Hi, Tess. Please, Alice is fine. I hear you might be interested in taking over NUTR 430 for me. That would be great.'

'Well, yes, Jacqui shared the course information with me. I do have one question. How open would you be to some changes to the syllabus?' Tess held her breath while she waited for Alice to respond.

'Uh, I don't see a problem with that. As long as you touch on what you think are objectives that will prepare them for – how do they say it in the standards manual? – 'essential knowledge and skills relating to professional practice,' I'd be fine with your changes. Maybe you can send me a draft of what you have in mind a couple of months before the course starts, too.'

Tess wondered if Alice had actually memorized the professional standards manual. She was becoming more and more intimidated. 'And what can I expect for remuneration?'

'Right. The current rate is about $5000, but you could expect a more official quote from the associate dean if we're going to move forward with your appointment.' Alice became more cool matter-of-fact as she realized that Tess was about to take on the course.

Tess knew she could use that extra money, as her husband had mentioned the previous week that he might be laid off for the summer. 'How many students are typically enrolled?' Tess felt obliged to ask one more question before accepting. She didn't want Alice to think it was only about money.

Tess could hear Alice smile in response to Tess's question. She knew it was a *fait accompli*. 'All of the fourth-year students are required to take the class, so there will be twenty-five registered. It's quite a nice size, actually.'

'Well, that sounds reasonable. Uh, I guess I'll do it.'

'Great! I'll have our associate dean draw up the paperwork. You should receive it within the week. Let's talk more after you've signed the contract.'

'Sounds good. OK, talk to you then.' As Tess hung up, she felt a mixture of excitement and panic. What was she getting herself into? Thankfully, Jacqui had agreed to spend some time with her to revise the reading list. Tess took a deep breath and thought to herself, 'An adventure, my dear. You can do it.' Finally, an opportunity to blend her practical knowledge with professional practice theory.

The months slipped by, as they do. Tess and Jacqui met in June to create a revised reading list and syllabus. They talked about the potential for this course to reach beyond the classroom walls, believing, as bell hooks does, that *knowledge and critical thought done in the classroom should inform our habits of being and ways of living outside the classroom* (hooks, 1994, p. 194). Teaching to transgress. Tess made arrangements for the readings to be available at the bookstore. Finally, the first day of class arrived. Tess was unusually calm. '*Think of it as an adventure …*'.

Chapter One – Unkept Promises

There is both sadness and adventure ahead,
and there is pain to pay for the somnambulant
beliefs in our own dominion.

(Jardine, 1998, p. 135)

Week 1: September 7

Dani slipped into class, quickly taking her seat near the back, always close to the door. Her long dark hair was messily swept up and held precariously with a single clip. Dani travelled light these days, probably a habit acquired while spending the entire summer at her parents' beachside house, where her skin and rhythm had both been kissed by the sun's easy warmth. The transition back to school was difficult, and a nine o'clock start didn't make it any easier. Settling into her unyielding plastic seat, Dani took a long drink of her warm coffee, no milk, no sugar, and looked to the front of the room. A new semester was about to begin.

'Good morning, everyone! Welcome. How was your summer?' A question not really seeking an answer. She quickly continued, 'This is NUTRITION 430: Orientations to Dietetic Practice. I'm Dr. Taylor. I'm usually the instructor for this course, but since I'm starting a research leave this month, I've arranged for someone else to be with you this term. Before we begin, I just need to check, did everyone get a copy of the course reader at the bookstore?'

Alice quickly scanned the room of fresh-faced young women as they all nodded, yes. She expected as much. Dietetic students were typically very well organized, ready in ways that often surprised her.

'Great. OK. As I mentioned, I'm not going to be with you this term, so allow me to introduce you to Tess Leung. She'll be sharing with you some of her experiences along with what looks like a pretty … interesting syllabus.' Alice paused, looked over to Tess, and smiled. Even though Tess shared her reading list with Alice months ago, Tess was sure that Alice hadn't actually read any of her selections.

'We're very lucky that Tess is able to be with you this term since she brings experience from community health and clinical practice. Tess is very active in our profession and I would add that she is dedicated to dietetic education. She has a Master's degree in adult ed from this very university. Right, Tess?'

Tess smiled as she nodded. Her calm demeanour a sharp contrast to Alice's crackling intensity. Dani studied Tess's somewhat bemused expression, wondering what it signified. Dani shifted in her chair. Alice continued, speaking even more quickly.

'Well, I'll let Tess say more about all that. I have to go, so I wish you all a great term.'

As Alice left the room, everyone took a much-needed breath, and all eyes shifted to Tess, standing next to the overhead projector. She was wearing a dramatic flowing dress, coloured in greens and blues. Tight around her neck was a dramatic string of large round red beads, like the ones Frida Kahlo wore. Dani had always secretly loved such beads and wished that she were bold enough to wear them around her slender neck. Tess's curly grey hair erupted erratically all over her head, her eyes sparkled and danced in a kind face punctuated by fine lines. Laugh lines, Dani's mom called them. Dani recalled watching her mother applying a mass of expensive creams and lotions to keep those lines at bay. Dani was brought up with the impression that laugh lines were undesirable, that the process of aging was to be defied. Clearly Tess wasn't living under similar tyrannies. Nor, apparently, was Tess susceptible to tyranny about body size. Under the soft folds of her flowing silk was a mature woman's body of clear substance, grace, and strength. As Tess began to speak, Dani found herself leaning forward, focused, strangely drawn to her, something about Tess.

'Good morning. Hello. Well, we have a very full term together, so I'm just going to jump right in with some introductory remarks.' Tess took a deep breath and stepped forward, shifting into her performance of university instructor. 'I feel compelled to tell you that our profession, the dietetics profession, is dying.' Tess's voice was soothing even though her words were not. She paused. 'Quite an outrageous statement, I know, and one that I'm not sure I believe is true. But, if it is true, if our profession is dying or experiencing what one of my colleagues calls a "living death," what should we be doing to revive and reconnect our profession to its life-sustaining vision?' Tess spoke slowly, measured tones of logic mixed with dramatic flare. Dani was transfixed, but not outwardly. Tess continued. 'OK. Maybe you're a cynic, or better, a pragmatist. You're wondering how you came to be admitted into a dietetics program if the profession itself is dying. What's in store for you? An important question, indeed. I can only say that perhaps it's a matter of economics, perhaps it's another matter entirely. Whatever the reason, it's not for me to judge. I feel obligated to tell you, though, that more than one of my colleagues has shared with me the opinion that our profession is dying.'

Dani was confused. What a peculiar way to begin a class. Was this some sort of problem-based learning case that Tess was setting up for the students? Where was she going with this? Dani invariably had strong responses to people – respect, contempt, or indifference. These responses arose from an immediate, mostly subconscious process of sorting, of ordering her world. Tess wasn't easily contained, though. This troubled Dani, caused her unrest.

'So, I'm here among other things to get your help.' Tess paused. 'Well, I'm concerned and since you have such a unique perspective, not terribly jaded by our profession's history, your ideas and energy are crucial. In your fourth year, you can see the light. You've worked hard to be here. I expect you're hopeful. If the profession is worth saving, we need optimists mapping our course. Of course, you would not be in this class if you were not exceptionally bright, resourceful, and capable. Look around you. Who do you see? As is the case in other dietetic programs, you are surrounded by women.' Tess stopped as the students looked around at each other.

'Is there diversity represented among you through culture, age, body size, class? This is what I intend to explore with you in our collective attempt to determine whether our profession is truly dying. But, before we go further, I'm curious. Why did you choose dietetics? What do you believe the promise of this profession to be?'

Meg, seated near the front, wasn't sure she understood the question. The promise of dietetics? What promise? She looked around the room and wondered what others were thinking. Impatient with silence, she put up her hand and asked Tess to clarify her question. Tess complied. 'When you think of yourselves in five, ten, twenty years, having been a dietitian for that entire time, what do you think your life will be like? What will dietetics have provided for you?'

With a far-off look on her face, Meg imagined her life in five years. She conjured a vivid image. She hoped to one day be working in a downtown eastside clinic supporting healthy eating among those with few material possessions. It was her dream. It was the only reason she chose dietetics.

Dani dreamed another image. Dani saw herself on TV, sharing the latest nutrition information with her loyal audience. She'd be wearing tailored suits, and her nails would be perfectly manicured. She'd speak intelligently and respond with ease to any nutrition question asked. When she wasn't hosting her popular morning TV show, she would work with athletes and the entertainment industry, high-powered people with glamorous lives who needed her advice. She would have a luxurious downtown office and would be well known, well respected, and well off.

Tess expected silence in response to her question. She was sure no one has asked these students such a question before. She tried to remember to be gentle with them, to ease into the process. It was their first class together and much was at stake in finding the tone that would support eager participation in future sessions. She invited students to take out a piece of paper and pen and for the next three minutes write up a description of the image of their dietitian selves in the future. She explained that they would be asked to share their writing, if they felt comfortable doing so, and that she hoped that they would share because it would make their time together that much more interesting to her and to others. She started timing, and the silence changed into something less burdensome, less formidable. Some students actually started writing, others stared out windows, and others checked life inscribed by Palm Pilots. One young woman named Candice took out her phone and started intently pushing buttons. Beep, beep ... beeeep. Electronic signals to tell callers she was temporarily not available. She slid the phone back into her exceptionally small, exceptionally pink leather bag and smiled meekly at Tess. Then, even she picked up her pen and started to write. While the clock ticked, Tess permitted her mind to drift. Oh, the experience of the first class, much like a first kiss, slightly awkward, leaning in this way, bumping, jostling, leaning that way, eager, willing. The anticipation of it all, a vision of flow and ease met with the reality of false starts, tension, groping for something familiar to anchor herself. It had been a very long time since Tess's first kiss, and yet she could still feel the rush of excitement for it, the desire to be right for these young women.

After five minutes, Tess looked expectantly out to the group and asked if anyone would like to share their thoughts. The briefest of pauses then, 'Uh, I will,' Meg carefully offered from the front row. Tess could see she had written a great deal. Who was this young, earnest woman wearing a tangle of brilliantly coloured cotton scarves around her neck and hair? All this a fine contrast to her simple t-shirt and jeans, a hole worn through at the knee. The discourse of Meg's appearance suggested that she had been places, had seen things that not everyone had seen, her scarves flamboyant markers of her travels. The thin cotton T and loose-fitting jeans suggested modesty, a woman not given to excess, not given to consumption read by the others' choice in clothes.

'Uh, I'm Meg, yeah, hi. Yeah, in five years I'm working in the downtown eastside, where I now volunteer with the Union Gospel Mission. You know, the people who provide turkey dinners at Thanksgiving? That's what I do. People down there need our help. Their lives are hard and I see myself helping them, helping to make things easier, providing better access to a safe supply of nutritious food.'

Tess heard the text of nutrition policy documents. She wondered if Meg had read those papers, given the script she was reciting. Tess pondered the political nature of changing existing food policies and her mind greyed with the enormity and challenge that she predicted for Meg's future. She could only feel that way given her previous experiences as a member of her community's food security task force. It seemed like so long ago that they initiated the process to ensure 'better access to a safe supply of nutritious food,' and yet nothing had really changed. Tess had spent months developing a 'local foods' food guide to assist in raising the profile of the cost of food and the challenge for people on limited incomes. She and her group had been presented an award in recognition for their efforts. Always the one to shift the focus off herself and onto issues, Tess had asked her colleagues heading her provincial dietetics association to feature the food guide in an upcoming newsletter and sign off on a press release to the media about her award. They refused, saying the topic was too controversial. That experience stung Tess for a long, long time. Only now could she talk about it without a spasm of frustration gnawing at her gut. And, ever the pragmatist, Tess realized that the work still needed to be done. Meg's dedication was faintly, briefly inspiring.

'How long have you been volunteering with the Mission, Meg?' Tess ventured, setting a precedent for respectful interactions, telling students she sincerely cared about what they said, that she cared about them.

'Uh, this is my third year. I want to keep going. I'm getting to know some of the people down there. Everyone is really nice. I really like it.'

Tess started to feel like Meg was trying to convince her of something, something of her identity was tied up in what Meg was saying, tied up like her scarves – bright, dynamic, honest. Tess marked the moment, once again smiling and meaning it.

'Thanks so much, Meg. Anyone else?' Tess invited, smoothly connecting with each student. Her eyes laid to rest on Dani in the back corner. Tess suddenly realized that Dani had been watching her quite intently the entire time, not bothering to write. Tess's eyebrows raised slightly in surprise and Dani was shaken from her reverie. She leaned back in her chair, wishing she could disappear, wanting to disappear into her vision of the future, wishing herself there without all this nonsense of school, wishing to make it, proving to everyone that she could make it.

'Some of you may have a clear vision without having to write it down,' Tess guessed. 'Please share it with us.'

Dani waded in, signalling to Tess that she would take her up on her offer to speak by image, not by text. 'I see myself sharing nutrition advice on TV, to reach the widest possible audience.' Tess knew there was much Dani was leaving out of this scenario and she knew this all too well because she'd seen it play out in almost every student and dietetic intern she had spent time with. The desire for visibility, for recognition. She recognized Dani's dream was more rooted in familial expectations than in her actually wanting to influence the public to eat better – that effect, improbable as it was, would be an added bonus. Tess needed to be cautious with her remarks to Dani, especially given the ubiquity of the fantasy. Why do so many women seek out dietetics as a means for being seen and heard? Hadn't they realized the contradictions in taking that path, with food work being the common domain of women and ostensibly invisible? Tess saw that an opportunity to teach was manifest in Dani's vision. She seized it.

'That is truly fascinating, Dani. What you are saying, if I interpret you correctly, is that people on TV have influence, powerful influence over TV viewers, and if our profession is to survive, to increase our profile, the more dietitians on TV sharing useful information about nutrition and food, the better for everyone. I wonder why is it that by our mere presence on TV, we are given instant credibility? Does anyone have a sense of why this is the case?'

Dani was taken off guard by Tess's enthusiasm. It was difficult for her to think straight and almost impossible for her to manage a response to Tess's questions. It seemed obvious to Dani that, since it was so difficult to get on TV, anyone who secured such a prestigious spot must have something important to say. Hadn't Tess watched other dietitians on TV? Didn't she get it?

Meg's voice interrupted Dani's thoughts. 'I think it has something to do with the letters, RD, registered dietitian. I don't know.'

'Are there people on TV talking about nutrition, healthy eating, who aren't RDs?' Tess was getting into it.

'Yeah, lots of people, but some of their advice is weird, non-scientific,' said Meg. Dani wanted to step in and defend her position even though she wasn't exactly clear where the conversation was going.

'OK. So, maybe it's not that being on TV leads to credibility, it's more about a professional designation. What do the letters RD signify to you?'

Dani was immediately irritated. How did they get on this topic? What was the relevance? The tone of her response reflected her impatience: 'It says that someone got an education in the science of food and nutrition and that their knowledge is superior to those who did not get that proper education. That's why we're here. RD says something to everybody about the kind of education, the kind of training we get, you know, a scientific nutrition education.'

'Again, very interesting, Dani. A perfect segue into your reading for next week – Kim Travers's 'Do You Teach Them How to Budget?' This is a challenging article and we will revisit it near the end of the term. With this first reading, please prepare a one-page written response to the question 'What does this text say that provokes you?' On the other side of the same page, please make a list of words that you had to look up in the dictionary. Yes, it's that type of article! We will start our next class with your responses to that particular question and any others you might have about the chapter. I think we should create an online glossary, too. Online would be best. I think Blackboard has some of these capabilities. I'll look into that. Oh, and I will expect you to hand your one-pager in to me at the end of our next class. I promise to return it on the 21st. This will count as your first reader-response submission.'

Tess checked her watch and noticed they still had ten minutes remaining, but felt it an appropriate place to finish for their first class. 'Alright, that's enough for today. Feel free to email me with your questions and I'll see you next week.' Tess gathered up her papers and waited for all the students to file out. She felt satisfied with how the class went and looked forward to meeting with Jacqui at the teashop for a debriefing. As she turned out the lights and closed the door, her thoughts took flight, a *theory of flight* (Rukeyser, 1935). Tess was swept up in the romance of teaching, the possibilities as they spun out in front of her, and the tensions that awaited. She felt certain that being there was the right decision.

ે♣

It was the summer of 2002, the first summer of Jacqui's doctorate and she had adventured into a seminar taught by Dr Rishma Dunlop, a recent doctorate in language and literacy education, teaching at York University. Women, Writing, and Imagination: Curriculum as Aesthetic Text. Jacqui was intrigued, tempted by theorizing on women, with women. Rishma's description of the course – an engaging mix of women and pedagogy, women and theory, women and aesthetics – woke in Jacqui a protracted longing for some absent thing, perhaps it was literature. They were to read Virginia Woolf's *A Room of One's Own*. In the lazy days before the course started, Jacqui read that volume voraciously, carrying the well-worn little book with her everywhere. It was the very first time she had read a course text (and a literary text, at that) before the course had started. It was to be a summer of firsts.

The class started in a chilly, windowless room. Rishma promised her students she would try to find them another, more aesthetically compelling space. Jacqui instantly trusted and relied on her to find that space to nurture their writing imaginations. Introductions from the students – all women, all brimming with the sense of something special about to unfold – their intuition strong, confident, and sure. Rishma distributed reams of readings from Lorde, de Salvo, LeGuin, Griffin, and Rich. Mesmeric female texts of which Jacqui imbibed. During class, Jacqui drifted away, imagining women writing, alone at their desks, wind billowing long, sheer cotton curtains. These women writers stared off into lush gardens, watching their children play, happy, luxuriating in their thoughts and their feelings, writing their lives.

Jacqui returned to fiery conversations of the erotic as power. She was suddenly jarred by the insistence that the erotic had a place in academia. The chapter before her was from Audre Lorde's *Sister Outsider* – *the aim of each thing we do is to make our lives and the lives of our children richer and more possible. Within the celebration of the erotic in all our endeavors, my work becomes a conscious decision – a longed-for bed that I enter gratefully and from which I rise up empowered* (Lorde, 1984). There was in the class discussion essential recognition and admiration for what Lorde evoked with those words. At once, anything was possible, richer and more promising.

Rishma guided them through the personal and the political, the erotic and the repressed. They responded emotionally and eagerly to her invitations to write poetry, while they wrestled with the praxis of collaboration. They told the truth about their lives and their worlds split open. A collaborative poem was inspired by Adrienne Rich, each student starting her stanza with 'Somewhere a woman is writing a poem.' The process was excruciatingly complex, selves born unto text and voice, autobiographies. On the last day of class, they taped themselves reading, polyphonic. Tears blurred their words, blurred their speaking – defiantly erotic, gently evocative. Months later, their choreopoem was accepted for publication in an online educational journal, and a small group of them, including Rishma, presented their collective work at an international education conference. Jacqui felt thrilled with the acknowledgment of her writing. Those fearful internal vixens attempting to silence her were themselves quieted as she sat at her desk, writing and writing, curtains blowing, her creative longing brimming to the surface. And she was not alone. Somewhere a woman was also writing a poem.

Jacqui's final project for Rishma's class was to be a personal essay taking into consideration her relationship and educational development as a woman in response to the work and influence of another woman. Like many others, she wrote about her mother. She poured on pages the subjective experience of coming out as a lesbian, although the category still discomfited her. An auto-episiotomy, bloody and painful, but the process, the writing, lifted her out of her shame. For the first time, she began to understand Lorde, who had said *once we know to which we are capable of feeling that sense of satisfaction and completion, we can then observe which of our various life endeavors bring us closest to that fullness.* From then on Jacqui was attached to the notion of her academic work as erotic, passionate, disruptive, and beautiful. Staying attached involved deep feelings of fear and risk, but, like Lorde, she considered that *our erotic knowledge empowers us* and that poetic musings can save lives, *and it is a grave responsibility not to settle for the convenient, the shoddy, the conventionally expected, nor the merely safe* (Lorde, 1984).

❧

Jacqui woke with a start and sat up immediately. Her daughter, Evyn, was crying out. She felt milk falling from her nipple onto her bare thigh and instinctively reached towards her breast to stem the flow. There was no milk. She was not leaking. These were phantom drops. She hadn't breastfed Evyn for several months. All her milk was gone. Insolent thoughts tricked her into believing she should still be breastfeeding her child. She stopped too soon, only six months. When asked by friends, family, and strangers, 'Are you still breastfeeding?' she would sheepishly admit, 'No,' and they would reply, 'Oh, well, six months will give her a good start at least.' It was most difficult to admit to her dietitian colleagues. Jacqui was well versed in the professional nutrition discourse insisting that breastfeeding is best for at least one year. And it wasn't as if she intended to stop after six months. It just happened. Jacqui herself had always thought mothers would be doing their best for their children if they breastfed. Period. It was their responsibility to the child. How judgmental and decontextualized! Until she had Evyn, her beliefs had been pointedly absolute. Recent research by her sister dietitians had reinforced these views. Now she was condemned by that discourse, a familiar guilt rooted through her gut, adamant, gripping tightly the vulnerable tissues of her heart. She lived with this feeling daily, her mother-guilt born of reductionist views on mothering.

She stood up and padded quietly to Evyn's room. It was 3:30 a.m. Kelly was fixing Evyn's bottle in the kitchen downstairs, clearly more attuned to her cries, waking first. Jacqui stood beside Evyn's crib, lowered the rail, and bent way down, her mouth on Evyn's cheek. 'It's OK, baby girl. Mommy loves you. Your milk is coming.' Jacqui started to sing in whispers. Evyn immediately stopped crying to hear her better.

There's a wee baby moon,
floating on her back,

with her silvery little toes in the air.
And she's all by herself in the deep blue sky,
but wee baby moon doesn't care
(Sho-Mo and the Monkey Bunch, 2004).

Jacqui tasted Evyn's tears on her lips. Evyn grabbed a handful of her hair and pulled her closer, demanding more whisper-singing.

The itsy bitsy spider climbed up the water ... spout.
Down came the rain and washed the spider ... out.
Out came the sun and dried up all the rain
and the itsy bitsy spider crawled up the spout again.

Evyn smelled sweetly of sleep, yeasty cereal, and fresh air. Jacqui could never get enough of her smell, of her. Her sturdy body was still until Kelly entered the room. She fully flexed in anticipation of her warm formula, pushing Jacqui away. Jacqui left the room quietly, so not to distract them from their routine, and slipped gratefully back into their bed. In only a few hours she had to get up and dash off to school, where she was trying to finish her dissertation. Sleep beckoned and Jacqui succumbed long before Evyn finished her milky, nourishing articulations in Mommy's loving arms.

ॐ

The tea shop was full, loud with students, as Jacqui watched Tess manoeuvre to meet her in the far corner. 'Hi, what are you having?' Jacqui asked, standing to greet Tess with a generous hug, full-bodied, just like her grandma had taught her. 'Oh, good hug! Um, peppermint tea, please.'
'I'll be right back.'
Tess sat and sighed. The first class was always richly intense, just getting a sense of the students, their expectations, giving

them enough to flavour the remainder of the term, but not too much as to reveal all the surprises. Tess likened it to a game, a performance, where everything was measured, yet within those confines was the possibility for play and artful communication of myriad interpretations. She envied other instructors who planned each class to the last detail, faithful to carefully worded learning objectives, mapping each step of their path through a four-month course. She had tried to be more like them, especially because she thought that was what was expected of her, but she always eventually slid off track, giving in to the flow of learning as it emerged from her and the students, often unpredictable, but always exhilarating. Funny, when she did open up and let go, she felt alive, more connected to everything around her – a lesson, to be sure.

Jacqui approached with the tea, carefully placing it on the table for Tess. A waft of steaming mint cleared their minds for conversation.

'Well, how was it? Details!' Jacqui leaned forward, eager to hear all about the first session.

'Well, it was what you might expect; all women, young, prepared, probably prepared for something completely different, but prepared!' The two women laughed, a sign that they were speaking a common language, a familiar refrain of educational experiences that were markedly predictable. Wiesel would describe their shared educational experience as one emphasizing *theories instead of values, concepts rather than human beings, abstraction rather than consciousness, answers instead of questions, ideology and efficiency rather than conscience* (Wiesel, 1990). They had been there and they laughed, nervously and knowingly – they didn't want to go there again.

'What did you get into?' Jacqui asked.

'Well, I shared with them the possibility that our profession is dying. I remember reading that in your research transcripts. Then I asked them to consider the "promise of our profession."' Tess was clearly excited by what had transpired. 'I just hope they are able to trust that we are going somewhere – that the process will unfold in due time.'

'I'm sure they are having some doubts, a healthy scepticism! You are inviting them into a darkness, unknown, uncharted waters. What's Alice like to work with?'

'Alice is very high energy, very rushed, very busy. I don't envy her. It seems like she has a lot going on. I guess she is submitting her application for tenure this year. God, that process sounds intense. Are you sure you want that for yourself?'

Jacqui wondered the exact same thing, misgivings about life as a faculty member. The academy can be very unforgiving, especially for women with children. Aware and undaunted, she thought it was the next step for her, the next challenge in her career. Being political and idealistic, Jacqui thought that with enough academic diversity, a critical mass would embrace multiple ways of being professor. Sometimes that dream seemed like empty, romantic rhetoric in the face of a rigid institutional process.

'I know,' Jacqui's tone grew contemplative. 'Why would I deliberately step into such politics, knowing what I know? Maybe, despite wanting it now, it won't happen. You know, not getting short-listed for one job already and now maybe two, I can feel myself speaking about other possibilities, maybe working with community organizations or developing my private practice more fully. I don't know. Last year, when my friend David got a job at the University of Arizona, something shifted for me – I saw what he accomplished, what an exciting turn his life took and I thought, I want that! It was a very energizing time, helped me get my comps finished, actually. Now, I don't know. It is hard to be a student in education without a discipline, or actually, with too many disciplines. It's hard for me to slot myself into job descriptions – am I a sociologist, educator, nutritionist, activist? Ha! Funny, talking about my identity as I work to explore, illuminate the identity of my dietitian friends. How ironic!' she laughed. Tess looked at her with empathy. She wanted Jacqui to be happy, but she knew the reality of her life – complicated, ambitious, resisting categorization.

'Hey, did I tell you the good news?' Jacqui asked, her enthusiasm returning. 'My first article was finally published – a chapter in a book! I just received a copy of it in the mail' (Gingras, 2004). Typically modest and reserved, Jacqui shared with Tess a small piece of what made her feel good and accomplished.

'Oh, how wonderful! What book? Show me. I want to read it. Maybe I can use it in the class.' Tess was sincerely thrilled.

'I'll show you next time we meet. It's great to see my work in print. It's like someone has affirmed that my thoughts count. I count.' Jacqui could hear those familiar themes from her research rising up into her consciousness again – the desire to be recognized, which was probably not specific to dietitians, but she had found to be common to participants in her research. She guessed they were all striving for some sense of being seen, being heard.

'You sound like Sally Field when she won her Oscar. You like me, you really like me!'

'Oh, God! I do, don't I?' Jacqui didn't like to admit her own desire for recognition, at least not now, after years of working through herself, through her emotional tenderness. She yearned to be honest but humble while acknowledging her accomplishments. It was a process ever unfolding.

'Oh, that reminds me, I want to bring up the notion of identity in class next week, but I'm not sure how. One of the students, when asked to share her vision of herself as dietitian in five years, told us she wanted to be on TV, sharing nutrition advice with the masses. It was actually great that she mentioned it because we were able to get into a discussion about what counts as 'sound, nutrition information' and who counts as 'nutrition expert.' At least that's where I would like us to go. I think the question I want to ask is, 'How does your identity influence your vision of self as professional?' What do you think? Does any of this make sense?'

Jacqui leaned forward, excited and thankful that the topic had shifted. 'What about a stream-of-consciousness writing activity where they respond to the question, 'Who are you?' or maybe you can 'construct' the identity of a registered dietitian with their input, their suggestions. Draw an outline on the board and ask them to fill it in with words, phrases, images. Could be really interesting. Take a digital photo – I'd love to see what you come up with.'

'Yeah, me too!' Tess sounded somewhat doubtful. 'Don't forget, Alice wants me to talk about my practice experience so students get a better idea of what they are getting into. That's the whole point of me being there.'

'We talked about this before, though, the sense of how our professional lives would be different if we had been invited to explore who we were as people, as women, before entering the profession. And how later on, it was really hard to reconcile the discontinuities, the discrepancies that we experienced. I wonder how the profession might shift if we would put more emphasis on self as interconnected, on the realities of professionalism, focused on feminist theory early on? Reminds me of that book by Judith Duerk (Duerk, 1999). She writes poetry interwoven with her lived experience as a facilitator of a woman's group. She repeats the line, 'how would our lives be different if …,' then she goes on to imagine just what might be different. Hey, maybe you could do that in class, too!' Jacqui suddenly noticed herself taking up too much space and she stopped with a start. Often, when she got really excited, eager for connection, she was met with only silence, the slow open of a vast, dark space between her and Other. It was a very lonely experience. She hoped that wasn't happening right then between Tess and her.

'Well, I don't know, Jacq. Sounds like I might be biting off more than I can chew with this one.' Jacqui sensed that Tess was in danger of feeling overwhelmed. She dialled back her enthusiasm.

'I think whatever you decide to do will be amazing. The last thing I want to imply is that what you already have planned isn't going to be brilliant and provocative. It will be, you will be, you always are.'

'Yeah, I know that. I know. I've got such a great opportunity here with these students. I don't want to waste it.' The strain written into the line of Tess's brow softened. She took the last sip of her tea and looked up, directly at Jacqui. 'I should go. I'm expected at work in half an hour. Traffic can be brutal.'

'Yeah, me too. Gotta get back to my writing.'

As Tess flung her shawl around her shoulders, she asked, 'How's it going, your writing?'

'Oh, not bad. Maybe you can help me with the editing! Actually, I would like your feedback on a couple things. If you're up to it we could chat while Zoë is at riding lessons one Saturday.'

They stood, shuffled their chairs out of the way, and hugged. Jacqui could smell Tess's citrus shampoo, her bergamot lotion, she took a deep breath, lingering. They disengaged, smiling. 'I'll email you later with a good date to meet at the stables. Hey, can you make a copy of your chapter for me to read?'

'Uh, yeah, if you want.' Jacqui made a mental note as she watched Tess leave, small regret intruding around the edges of her consciousness – she must be more attentive to Tess. Even though Tess had an aura of selflessness and wisdom, she needed time to be heard, too. Jacqui wondered who comforted Tess in the dark moments, who supported her through uncertainty and misgivings. She felt a warm wave of gratitude at simply knowing Tess and being able to share her true self with this incredible friend.

Jacqui's thoughts quickly turned to her writing – *a research reverie*. She was working through transcripts from her research workshops. At three different times, participants came together to discuss themes related to her research. At the first workshop, she remembered how one of the participants, Angela, described donning a 'cloak of dietetic education' as a means of staying out of connection with others. She talked about how appealing 'legitimate knowledge' was to her when she was young and how that drew her into the dietetic profession. Jacqui remembered the nods from the other participants as Angela shared her reflections. Angela explained that her efforts since then had been to shed that cloak, to work at self-connection, to learn who she was as a means to help others shed their own protective garb.

In the moment of silence after Angela spoke, Jacqui decided to describe her own work with women struggling with food and body. Starting hesitantly, she took the risk of being authentic and vulnerable. Jacqui described the most precious time in her work – the intermittent joyful moments when connection was so intense that her heart felt like it might explode. Was that joy also compassion or expansiveness? Perhaps all of that simultaneously. Those were the silent sacred moments of her work that Jacqui rarely attempted to put into language, because to do so would ultimately diminish the experience. Jacqui feared she would be misunderstood. Even in that moment of sharing with her colleagues, Jacqui felt that familiar radiance in her chest. She was in connection with her sister dietitians because she risked enough to share her own vulnerability.

Corine broke the silence by wisely asking the group, 'How many have been on the receiving end of that type of experience Jacqui described?' The tape in Jacqui's mind still echoed the quiet response Yasma offered, 'I would say I was.' She continued to tell her story. 'When Jacqui was describing her experience I could just remember the interview Jacqui and I had a few weeks ago for her research and how she was feeling with what I had to go through. I could just feel I was bonding with her. She was really feeling what I was going through. She was really caring. I was on the receiving end. Yeah, I could feel that.' Jacqui was taken by surprise to hear Yasma remember their time together. It was true. Jacqui had been deeply touched by Yasma's story of 'accomplishing the Canadian experience,' her tale of what happened when she moved to Canada from Iran – what amounted to cultural assimilation, in Jacqui's view. Jacqui was disappointed in herself for her silent complicity in the process. She felt profound sadness and *pain to pay for the somnambulant beliefs in her own dominion.* She told Yasma how touched she was by her story. And now, to know Yasma had been moved that way, that her heart too might explode to be heard in that way, made Jacqui tingle. She realized that this research would change her irrevocably. She was coming to know herself through dietitian Others. There was adventure ahead.

Chapter Two – Emotional Ecology

The old pedagogies will no longer do in the face of the ecologies
of flesh and bone and breath and the Earth's dear heart, torn.

(Jardine, 1998, p. 135)

Week 2: September 14

'Hey, Dani!' Meg offered an upbeat greeting to Dani as she entered the class.

'Wow, you're here early!' Dani was still struggling to get her bearings though it had been over a week since the term began. Why did it seem so challenging for her? She wanted to get things under control, in order. She vowed that she wouldn't go out again tonight and instead would try to catch up on her reading. She had barely finished the paper that Tess had asked them to read for today's class and she really wasn't sure she understood it at all, especially its relevance to her future career as a dietitian. How long was this charade, this colossal waste of her time, going to continue before she would complain to Dr Taylor about Tess and her approach to teaching? One more week, tops.

'Uh, yeah, I guess I'm a morning person. Always have been,' Meg admitted.

'Oh, yeah, right. I'm just going to grab a seat. Talk to you later.' Dani retreated to her customary seat in the back, by the door. Meg observed it was like Dani *needed* that seat, *had* to sit there. Meg was slightly intrigued with Dani and slightly intimidated. She wondered what Dani thought of her and she wasn't used to really caring what others thought. It seemed futile.

It was still a few minutes before nine and students were trickling into the classroom. Tess had arrived at eight o'clock so she might have some privacy before class began to focus on her lesson plan and to centre herself.

Jacqui had recently shared with Tess her theories on guest lec-turing as marginalized use of women's professional knowledge. Guest speakers were very common in the dietetics curriculum, probably as a result of the complaints from practitioners that new graduates, despite the knowledge they had acquired in the classroom, were unprepared for the experience of being a dieti-tian. A simple remedy, invite the practitioners into the classroom to share with students what their work was really like and how it related to the textbooks or not. Tess felt honoured to be asked to work with dietetic students, and she felt that such guest lectures were her way of giving something back to the profession. She could always decline the invitations, but she enjoyed the interac-tions with students, the satisfaction it gave her to be teaching. Tess had never felt marginalized by the faculty members who had invited her to speak. Besides, she had always wanted to be a teacher and was disappointed that she had never been able to secure a teaching position after she finished her masters degree.

She remembered her father's saying something derogatory about teaching, encouraging her instead to apply to medical school. Tess could not bear the thought of medicine – so much pressure, so little time for family life, for other creative pursuits. Instead of doing what was colloquially called 'pre-med,' but re-ally amounted to a science degree, Tess chose dietetics, assuring her father that she would apply to medicine when she finished her degree. She never did. She considered dietetics a compro-mise, one made secretly, without her father's consent. At the time she had had no idea what the practice of dietetics was all about. She found it revealing to her that many of her dietitian friends started out in much the same way, accidentally choosing dietet-ics because of its scientific legitimacy, because of their interest in food and health, but not truly understanding what dietetic practice would have in store for them.

She was determined to explore this very dilemma with the stu-dents today, following up on the themes of the first class. She hoped that her centring ritual had shifted the energy in the room to allow her clarity of vision, for without well-fashioned lesson plans, clarity of vision was her most cherished teaching asset.

'Good morning, everyone. Let's get started. A couple things to get to today. As promised during our last class, we are going to continue our conversation about "the promise of our profession" and get into Travers's paper, and then you can hand in your reader responses to me at the end of class. Can someone start us off with one of your responses?'

Silence.

Tess waited, idly arranging papers in front of her, trying not to intimidate the students into speech, but not wanting to appear too distracted, off-hand, or uninterested.

'Yeah, the paper, the budget paper, it was really impossible to understand.' It was the small voice of the red-haired student, Candice. Then, as if on cue, several other voices blurred together in agreement. Obviously, a very good place to begin.

'I agree,' admitted Tess. 'It is a very difficult text and Dr. Travers – now Dr. Raine actually … in this piece of writing, Dr. Raine has something very important to offer us.'

Yeah, but if we can't understand her, what's the point?' Stacy moaned.

'Troubling clarity,' Tess mused. 'There is a point to troubling clarity. Let me ask you this. When someone asks you what you're studying in school and you say nutrition, is it not common for that person to start asking you all sorts of nutrition-related questions like, "What should I eat to lose weight? Are carbs really that bad for me? Is organic better?" This happens to me. Anyway, my point is that people already believe they know what you do and what you know when you say "nutrition" or "dietetics." Dietetic knowledge, because it relates to food and eating, everyday, common behaviours, is assumed to be uncomplicated, simple. Everybody is already a nutrition expert because of their access to nutrition information through media and also because everybody is already an eater. If you haven't already had this experience, do a little experiment. Ask your friends and family what it is they think dietitians do and see how they respond. OK. So, how does any of what I'm saying relate to Travers's article? Well, when difficult language is used to explain a theory or a phenomenon, readers must read it differently; they are called to engage more closely; things are not as they appear. The astute reader will recognize that Travers has used a rhetorical device called irony. She discusses the way nutrition discourse, the language professionals use to talk about nutrition, excludes some recipients of that nutrition information because it is connected to an ideology of individualism and expertise. In the same way, she has excluded some of her readers from the knowledge she attempts to share. I don't know if this was intentional, but it has a very profound impact when we come to see it in a different light.'

Silence.

'So, is there anyone willing to attempt to summarize what the article was about, adding to what I've already said?'

A longer silence.

Then Meg took up the challenge. 'My roommate is in sociology and she is studying Foucault and stuff, so I asked her to decipher some passages for me and she said the author is putting down the way dietitians are trained, that the training is a problem because they ... we learn facts and not how to apply those facts in real-life situations.'

'Do you agree with your roommate?'

'Uh, sorta. In some classes it's all about memorizing stuff, at least it has been up until now. I think some of our third- and fourth-year classes will be different. But really, I'm not a dietitian yet, so I don't really know for sure. What do you think?' Meg felt secure and on steady ground with her opinions and question. She had always wondered why she had to take organic chemistry and physics. She was eager to get on with the community nutrition courses, and she loved problem-based learning, even though she was one of the few who would actually admit it.

'My experience is that I was not prepared for the type of work that I'm currently doing. Now is this because what I'm doing is specialized practice? Perhaps. I've spoken with new grads, and most of them say that they are well prepared for their work as clinicians. We might consider that there are different spheres of practice, like entry-level, advanced, non-traditional. So is it possible for a four-year undergrad degree and one-year internship to prepare someone for all spheres of practice? Well, I don't think so, nor should it. However, the story doesn't necessarily end there.' Tess paused. The students were quiet but seemed to be paying attention.

Then an intrepid student sitting at the back of the room asked, 'What does *discourse* mean? Why doesn't Travers just use the word *language* instead?'

'Good question. Does anyone have a response to that?'

Meg flipped through her highlighted copy of Travers's paper and pointed to a passage, 'On page 214, she says, discourse is "the system of language and conventions that make the knowledge of a particular discipline possible." So, I guess what she's trying to say is that discourse is a special type of language, a disciplinary language. Yeah, she's using discourse, too.'

'Exactly, Meg. Your roommate would probably call it sociological discourse, but every discipline has its own discourse – it makes possible a field of knowledge, to paraphrase Foucault. It is also important to emphasize, as Travers does a little further down that same page, that discourse determines what "counts" as valid knowledge within the discipline.' Dani, I remember what you said last week about the image of yourself in five years and how that took our conversation to a similar theme of "what counts" for valid nutrition information on TV. My point in bringing this up again is to permit us to consider and reflect on our own use of nutrition discourse as ideological. How would you define the term *ideological*?'

Heads down, silence.

'Um, if I'm interpreting this moment of silence correctly, I struggle with defining *ideological*, too, yet it might be helpful to note that ideologies are all around us. Let's start with a definition.' Tess noticed polite smiles cross students' mouths. She continued, turning around, picking up a piece of chalk, referring to notes in hand, and wrote on the blackboard.

'According to Merriam-Webster's online dictionary, an ideology is a) a systematic body of concepts especially about human life or culture, b) a manner or the content of thinking characteristic of an individual, group, or culture, c) the integrated assertions, theories and aims that constitute a sociopolitical program. Travers points out that ideology, discourse, and power are related.' Tess read from Travers's text. 'At the top of page 215, Travers writes, "It is the ideological, and hence, seldom questioned, dimension of discourse that contributes to its power in social organization." Let's try to extend this concept to our own lives. As registered dietitians, RDs, we are being educated to use a specific language regarding food, a language we are learning in our biochemistry, physiology, and clinical nutrition courses. I think we agree that the language we are using is nutrition discourse and we have a pretty good idea about what 'counts' as knowledge in our field. We construct knowledge claims by reading scientific journal articles and either adopting or rejecting the ideas that they offer. Because we use mostly scientific journal articles to construct our nutrition knowledge base, our discourse is ideological. Because we are educated professionals identifiable by the initials RD, "a privileged class" of health professionals, as Travers puts it, we use our discourse to represent our very specialized nutrition knowledge and to distinguish ourselves from those whose discourse, whose knowledge, is different, which in turn gives us power among those who might not understand our discourse. So, who are we trying to distinguish ourselves and our knowledge from?'

'Naturopaths.'

'Chiropractors.'

'Nurses.'

'Pharmacists.'

'Nutritionists.'

'Herbalists.'

The students seemed to be clear about who they were not. Tess nodded as the list grew. Candice elaborated, excited to be contributing to a discussion she finally understood, 'My mother's friend was talking yesterday about the acupuncture treatment she is getting for her migraines and how the so-called doctor started telling her what foods she should eliminate from her diet. She basically can't eat anything. The guy is a freak, a quack. He barely speaks English. I don't understand how people like that can practise in Canada.

Tess felt something sharp turn in her gut, a little terror chilled her heart, and she felt the need to put her hand on the desk to steady herself. She was instantly uncomfortable with how quickly students had come to understand and speak the practice of ideological domination. She felt disquieted by their words used to display dietetics' power-over other professions; more hegemonic than ideologic, more pejorative than emancipatory.

Dani noticed Tess's smile slowly disappear and sensed something was about to shift. The classroom grew quiet after a burst of noise and energy.

'Does anyone else find this discussion ironic?' Tess asked quietly. 'We need to stop here for a moment.'

Tess paused, closed her eyes, and took a deep breath. The students waited, concerned.

'It is very important to recognize that what I'm about to say next is not personal, but contextual. It isn't about who you are, it's about what was said,' Tess gestured to Candice. 'And we are to proceed with great care.' Tess had the students' rapt attention and for all the wrong reasons. She wished she could go back and start the discussion another way.

'I'm going to take responsibility for setting up your responses. I wish I could redo that, but I can't. Let's move forward from here. I feel a little overwhelmed by the words just spoken, but I think we can all agree they are a powerful example of ideological discourse that has the power to discriminate. There are very good reasons some of us hold these beliefs about others. We must explore how it happens that we hold these beliefs about people who are different, and this seems like a really good time to venture into that awkward space.' Tess chose her words carefully, attempting to be with her mixed feelings and be with the students at the same time. She had never experienced such a discussion before, but had prepared for it in theory. She wondered if this was what they meant by praxis.

'When we believe we are different from others, it becomes quite easy to make others wrong, especially if we believe that we are better. I think that's what nutrition discourse and ideology create – the potential for discrimination. I would like to hear from others. What did you hear? How are you feeling about this discussion?' Tess made the offer thinking that it will be almost impossible to stimulate dialogue at this point, with the tone of the class as it was. She waited and hoped.

Marci took up Tess's invitation. 'Uh, that was sorta hard to hear. My parents don't really speak English very well either. They're not doctors or acupuncturists or anything like that, but they don't speak English. I speak only Cantonese at home. Sometimes I don't feel welcome in Canada and to hear that comment kinda confirms my belief that Canada isn't as great as everyone believes it to be. Sometimes I wish my family had never moved here.'

Tess wanted desperately to keep this from getting too personal, to find a way to detach the students and herself from further trauma. 'I really appreciate you sharing that, Marci. And, again I want to say that it is important to consider what conditions are necessary for discrimination to occur so we might learn from our mistakes and avoid hurtful comments in the future. Does anyone else have anything to say at this point?'

Meg looked down at her notebook as she spoke. 'As hard as it is for me to admit, I've had those same thoughts about other people who claim they are nutrition professionals. Up until now, I haven't realized how ugly my thoughts were. I don't want to think like that anymore. It is not very inclusive. It's not who I am.'

'Yes, it's hard to see ourselves in less than flattering ways. However, if the comment hadn't been spoken, we would have missed this opportunity for seeing things differently. I would like to leave this important topic for the time being, but I ask that you maybe do some writing about this experience and what it has brought up for you.' Tess sensed that the students were relieved to be moving out of that uncomfortable space. Tess wondered if she moved along too soon, but she was also relieved.

'What do you think the author intends us to do with the information she has presented in this paper?' Tess heard her voice speak words, but it was like she was watching herself from above. She felt tense in her jaw and shoulders. Her breathing was shallow and her heart raced. She wondered if this counted as embodied curriculum. *She knew the old pedagogies would no longer do in the face of flesh and bone and breath. At stake was a transformative healing of their Earth's torn heart.*

'Well, since I couldn't understand it, I felt kinda helpless when I finished reading it. I have no idea what she wants me to do,' Candice complained.

'Yeah, me neither!' Another echo of dissent.

Dani had an idea. 'Maybe that's her point. When nutritionists try to teach low-income moms how to budget their money better, it just leads those moms to feel helpless and probably guilty. If they really don't have enough money, it makes no sense to teach them how to budget it better. I think that's Travers's point, right? The moms might already know how to budget, but the expert comes in and tells them by implication that they aren't doing it right.'

'What you are describing, Dani, is an ideology of individual responsibility. It's their individual responsibility to acquire the skills – say budgeting – even though possessing those skills will not ultimately help them feed their children or themselves any more healthfully. Indeed, the moms might know how to budget, but they don't have enough money to make a budget relevant. So what if the information that the expert shares is not useful or if it's something that the individual has heard before and tried with limited success? What then?'

'Well, that person might get really disillusioned, angry. I don't know.' Dani responded.

'So, while that single mom is busy trying to budget her money, she still has to feed her babies, clean the house, go to work, arrange for babysitters, wash the dishes, cook food, do laundry, pay the bills, shop for food, feed her babies, clean the house, and so on. You get the picture. Realistically, budgeting is not the best use of her time! And, I would add, it's unethical of those who claim to want to help her to suggest that she should learn to budget better in the first place.' Tess recognized the deep insult, the slap in the face, behind teaching people to budget when their lives were inextricably difficult and it was through no fault of their own that the money they did receive was inadequate to cover the most basic costs of living.

'Let's stop for a moment and imagine. I would like you to respectfully step into this woman's life, as fully as you can. Please take out a piece of paper, a pen, and write a letter to me, assuming I'm the one who is encouraging you to budget your money better, telling you to do it for your own good. Tell me how you feel about everything. Be honest with me. I think I deserve to know. You have two kids, one is turning two, running all around, getting into things, and the other is only six months, still very much needing your full attention, just about sitting up on her own. You are exhausted, still trying to breastfeed because you know that is best for your baby, but you can't get enough rest to replenish your body's supply of milk. Your boss is starting to get really put out by your frequent absences and late arrivals to work, which can't be helped because the daycare that both your children attend opens at 8:30 a.m. and you are expected to be at work at 8:00. Your mother helps out when she can, but she is not very reliable because she has health problems of her own. Your husband left you fourteen months ago, and you are in the process of divorce, not to mention the legal process of trying to collect child support. You are feeling alone, burdened, and there doesn't seem to be any relief. Now here you are, sitting with me, and all I can suggest is that you simply must budget your money more carefully. What is your response?'

❧

'Jane, I'm worried. I'm feeling at a loss for words.'

Jacqui sat in her office, on the hard chair. Jane, a young woman seeking nutrition therapy support, sat uncomfortably at the edge of the cozy sofa. She was terrifyingly thin. Jacqui had sat with her each week for the last three months, watching her slowly deteriorate, watching her disappear before her very eyes. Today, the brutal reality of her starvation was looming like death above and around them. Jacqui was not only at a loss for words, she was struggling to stay grounded. She was working as hard as she ever worked to stay connected to Jane in this moment. These were terrifying moments. Jacqui didn't know what to do except to try to stay connected and present with Jane.

'I know. Me too,' Jane whispered in reply. Her skin pulled tight across her cheekbones, her clothes hung off her, many sizes too large now. Her body was small, fragile. Jacqui could see that even in the short time that she'd worked with Jane, her body had changed dramatically. 'Oh, my God!' repeated over and over in her mind.

'The doctor at the hospital says that I'm "an urgent case." I guess I should be relieved by that, but it sucks to hear it. I just want to get better, but I can't do it on my own. It is too hard.' Jane looked down, dejected.

'Are you still going to classes?'

'Yeah, it gets me away from the house, from my mom and dad's fighting and constant watching. School is getting harder for me, though. The other day, a woman in one of my classes told me that I should try eating something cause I'm getting too thin. I don't even know her. I felt totally ashamed. Don't people get it? I'm trying, but the voice in my head is too loud. I can't let myself eat. How many others are watching me, noticing my body? I can't bear the thought of eating with anyone right now. I feel too exposed.'

'When do you feel most supported, comforted, peaceful?' Jacqui grasped for anything.

Jane didn't answer her right away. By the furrow across her brow, Jacqui guessed that she was concentrating, trying to think of the last time she had felt any of those things. Maybe Jacqui shouldn't have asked her that question. What if she never felt comforted or supported? How might that realization affect her mood, her state of mind, her ability to take care of herself?

'Um, well, I guess when I'm with Rachel I feel a little better.' Rachel was her closest friend and the woman who drove her to all her appointments and sat with her while she attempted to eat the little she was able to eat those days.

'Is Rachel here today?'

'Yeah, she's waiting for me in the car.'

'How would you feel if I invited Rachel in for a moment so we can all talk together?'

'Uh, OK. I mean, if she wants to. Should I go get her?'

'Yeah, let's go see if she wants to join us.' Jacqui was guided at this point by intuition. After weeks of working diligently on meal plans and exploring Jane's barriers to healing her relationship with food, Jacqui was willing to try something different. She had never done this before, but she thought working outside the box might help in this instance. Jacqui could see that Jane was running out of time. Both women were fearful. Jacqui made the effort to confront her fear by trying an unusual approach.

Jane and Rachel entered the counselling office together. 'Hi, I'm Jacqui. Please come in, have a seat. Thanks so much for joining us.' Jacqui motioned Rachel to sit beside Jane on the couch and closed the door gently behind them. Getting up to close the door gave Jacqui a few extra seconds to figure out what she was going to say. She took her time sitting down. She still didn't know what to say.

Silence.

Rachel and Jane smiled at each other. It was a new experience for them, too.

'Jane, what is it about your time with Rachel that you find comforting, supportive?'

'Well, you know, she is my closest friend, not judging me. I can be most myself with her.'

'Rachel, what do you see going on with Jane? Is it OK if I ask her this, Jane? Are you OK with this?'

'Yeah, I'm OK. I don't have any secrets from Rachel.'

'Well, Jane comes from a pretty ... her family is pretty intense. At my house, things are different, very different. I can kinda understand how hard it is for Jane ... hard for her to be at home. Her mom is pretty intense. It's chaotic, not ... not the best environment.' Rachel spoke in faltering sentences, carefully watching Jane's face for clues about what and what not to tell Jacqui, and not entirely convinced that it was alright for her to open up about such matters.

'How much time are the two of you able to spend together these days?' Jacqui asked.

'Well, maybe two nights a week. I'm going to Rachel's after our session. I'll stay the night and then I have to go home and get ready for school. I wish it was more, don't you?' Jane looked over to Rachel.

Rachel nodded. 'It could be more, you know. Why don't you stay Sunday night, too? We could figure something out.' Rachel's voice pleaded. They both knew that Jane's staying an extra night would not make her better, but it was a little thread of something, a little thread to hang onto.

'Maybe.' Jane was noncommittal. As much as she hated going home, she was needed there and believed that she should be there to take care of her nine-year-old brother. He had been acting erratically lately, too. The school called her house yesterday, leaving a message for her parents that Brandon had not shown up for class. 'Yeah, I'll tell them. Thanks for calling.' Jane tried to sound responsible, but just like everything else, she was barely keeping it together. This was the first time the school had called, but Jane knew it wouldn't be the last. Brandon's life was starting to unravel, her own unravelling was already well underway. Jane was consumed with fear that her mom would not be there to take care of him, that she might pass out and that her cigarette would start a fire, or, worse, that she would be driving him around town while drunk. She felt instantly sick at the thought. Jacqui noticed her face blanched.

'Jane, where did you just go?' Jacqui asked gently. She saw panic and tension sweep across Jane's face. Jane's emotions were in some ways that much easier to read these days. There was no place for them to hide, no soft recesses, no luxury of fading into the background.

Looking into Jacqui's eyes, Jane could no longer contain her despair. 'I'm worried about Brandon. I need to be home for him, but I can't. He needs me. He's just a little boy. I feel like I'm failing him, too. How did this happen to me?' Jane looked down, bereft. Jacqui felt overwhelmed. Waves of compassion washed over her. This was so hard. 'Jane, what is it that you need right now? Jacqui asked. She could see Jane's tears falling down gaunt cheeks. The three of them sat very still. Jane didn't answer. She despaired without words, Rachel's arm protectively around her shoulder. 'Take a breath, Jane. Tell us what you are feeling.'

Jane swiped away a tear from her face and looked at Rachel then at Jacqui. 'I'm feeling overwhelmed with it all. I need some time away.'

Rachel piped up. 'Why don't we go get Brandon and bring him over to my place, too?'

Jane lifted her head, looking hopeful. 'Hmmm. Yeah, that would be cool.' She checked her watch. 'He's just finishing his tutoring session. We could pick him up before he gets on the bus for home.'

Jacqui sensed Jane's hope and felt relieved. 'Maybe you could treat Brandon to dinner?'

Jane smiled. 'Maybe, Jacqui. Maybe.'

Jacqui could feel the tension shift and she thought for at least this moment, Jane would be OK. At least that's what she hoped.

⁂

A slight chill was in the air that Saturday morning as Jacqui walked to meet with colleagues to discuss the possibility of their group supervision. Clinical supervision of practitioners was a common practice in the mental health fields, often mandated. The supervisor assumed a variety of roles including teacher, counsellor, and consultant. Those practitioners seeking supervision were generally willing to reflect on their desire to learn skills and knowledge, explore personal dynamics and reactions to clients, and discuss ideas and questions on a collegial level. The idea of meeting to share professional practice issues came out of her research conversations with colleagues. Jacqui remembered Doris sharing how she envied her mental health colleagues for having that kind of peer support, while Valerie added with a smile, 'Maybe there's a new career path for you, Jacqui. Facilitating supervision groups for dietitians.' Jacqui was more interested in being a recipient of supervision, given her own challenges in practice.

A colleague asked Jacqui, 'Why is it called "supervision"? Seems rather hierarchical, doesn't it?' It did seem hierarchical, and Jacqui believed traditional modes of supervision to be disempowering on many levels. Having had an experience of a different sort with a wonderful therapist during her days co-facilitating support groups for women with a counsellor friend, she was firmly convinced that all clinical supervision didn't have to be demeaning and unproductive. Maybe just changing the name 'supervision' was all that was needed. Maybe 'facilitated professional support groups' would be a better choice.

At the outset of each supervision meeting, any immediate needs of the practitioners (e.g., crisis situations) or the clinical supervisor (e.g., ethical dilemmas) became a priority (Pearson, 2001). These needs are all things the group would consider before actually engaging in supervision. Jacqui believed that supervision activities depended on trust, a respect for professionalism, an awareness that not everything can or must be measured, and the reality that, in promoting supervision with all its inherent contentiousness, they as professionals were called to walk on a knife's edge (Launer, 2004). This particular form of support was a means for confronting the complexity of ongoing life in their everyday dietetic practice. Supervision was, after all, a meeting of two (or more) people, a shared possibility for each of them (Coles, 1989, p. 8). Jacqui opened the door to her office, which she had offered as a meeting space for the group. The aesthetics of intricate Indian wall hangings, brilliantly coloured pillows, large fronds of greenery, and a lively arrangement of reeds in a square glass vase on a low table immediately brought to mind memories of all the clients she had worked with over the years. Clients … The word to her was more than troublesome given its association with consumption and consumerism and, of course, capitalism, patriarchy … Where did it end? Instead, she preferred to speak the words 'women' or 'men' to describe those who sought her nutrition therapy services. Sometimes she still slipped, even with the sound of the word breaking at the back of her throat, she uttered 'client' to then hear herself disclaim and explain. Language burdened.

Tess arrived first. She was, as usual, flamboyant in ocean blues, prismatic violets, a spectrum of turquoise beads lighting her throat and greening her eyes. Jacqui and Tess greeted each other with a hug. 'Would you like some tea? Madagascar Vanilla Roiboos or Honeybush Peach?' Jacqui asked.

'Yum, I'll try the peach,' Tess answered as she settled into a luxuriously comfortable couch, a spot where so many women sat before her, spilling their impossibly painful life stories. Could a couch contain the gravity of their stories, those told and those yet to be revealed?

'How was your week?' Jacqui asked from the bathroom, where she was filling the kettle. 'How is the teaching going?' She was aware they hadn't spoken since Tess's first class.

'Yeah, it's going. We got into some pretty heavy stuff last class. Of course, I always wish I could go back and respeak my responses. We were talking about the 'Do You Teach Them How to Budget' article by Kim Raine and our conversation on language led to a conversation on difference, which actually led to a really discriminatory remark about who should be "allowed" to practise dietetics in Canada.'

'Oh, God, what did you do?' Jacqui returned from starting the tea and was sitting in a low-slung, golden-upholstered chair, the one she typically used. It is clearly a comfort for her, taking her place, in her office, as an authority. She made a dashing mental note to sit elsewhere next time.

'Well, I didn't do anything right away. I was in shock! I think I remember taking a deep breath and closing my eyes for a moment. That must have freaked out the students.'

'Well, it probably did get their attention. While you were taking a breath, they were holding theirs.' Jacqui wished she could be centred in those moments of praxis when everything she had read and theorized came into being, those rare moments of luminosity, ripe with possibilities for learning. 'Damn, I wish I could remember to be more still and meditative in those moments. My emotions tend to get the better of me.' Jacqui imagined her emotions as cunning little people, trying to trick her somehow into pedagogic missteps.

'I think that happened to me, too. After only a few comments from students, I took the opportunity to move on to another subject. It was like I was running away a little bit. What should I do? Maybe say something about it at the next class?'

'I might, after having more time to reflect and maybe write something down for myself to refer to so I can say as much or as little as I need to say. But listen to me, easy to take this role when I'm not standing there at the front. There is an amazing article by

Renee Norman and Carl Leggo (Norman & Leggo, 1995) about such experiences in the class. I'll email you the PDF version.'

'That would be helpful, thanks.' Tess smiled, and just then the kettle clicked off, signalling the water was ready. Jacqui stood with a sigh, back aching from spending far too much time writing at the computer, and returned to the bathroom to make a cup of Roiboos for herself and Honeybush for Tess. She had been thinking about what happened to her this week and wondered if the group would permit her some time to share with them her feelings and thoughts about it. Spending time reflecting had not lightened the experience for her, and she hoped sharing it with trusted friends would help ease the hurt.

'Oh, I think I hear Ariana and Gabrielle.' Tess got up to greet them and Jacqui ran the tap to boil more water for tea.

಄

'Nobody said it was easy ...' Chris Martin, lead singer for Coldplay sang out to Jacqui's conference audience. She had the song *The Scientist* (Martin, 2002) turned up loud. 'No one said ... it would be this hard. Oh, take me back to the start.'

Jacqui first heard *The Scientist* in one of her graduate classes, a course called 'Living Interpretations: A Hermeneutical Inquiry.' She remembered how the words tremored inside her, speaking directly to her ongoing trials as a dietitian, as a nutrition scientist, wishing things to be different, more human and beautiful. Since that very first time, the song lingered and continued to inspire her. She decided to offer it to a conference audience as a way to further explore what it evoked about identity in others. She had never played a song during a conference presentation before and wondered how people would respond.

After the song ended, Jacqui invited those in attendance to share with her what they thought the song meant, to perform a hermeneutics on the text of song lyrics. A studious-looking woman who sat close to the front put up her hand. 'You know,

I've never heard this song before and the context you provided has me slightly distracted, but I was very moved by it. Something, I'm not quite sure what, but is he trying to say something about anorexia?'

'Hmm, interesting. I've never thought of that before.' It was vaguely surprising to Jacqui given her work with women who struggled with eating disturbances.

'Have you seen the video?' asked a white-haired man dressed in a suit and tie. He spoke with a British accent, his glasses perched on the end of his nose.

'Yes, I have.' Jacqui, her stereotypes in full bloom, wondered what brought him to a conference on qualitative methods.

'It certainly changes the meaning for me. He wants to get back to the start to prevent his girlfriend from getting killed in a car accident. It's very eerie, powerful.'

The way he stated his version of the meaning suggested that there was only one. Jacqui offered that even for those who had seen the video, there were still multiple ways to interpret the visual and lyrical texts. The discussion was lively but, like most conference sessions, over too quickly, just scratching surfaces of curiosity. After she finished, several people approached Jacqui to share their email addresses with her. 'We should talk,' one young woman said, leaning in close, conspiratorially, wild red hair cascading down her back, 'I'm at the University of Victoria. My work in the School of Child and Youth Care is strikingly similar to what you describe in dietetics. Here is my card. Would you like to come to our conference next spring?'

&

Tess read from her paperback copy of Mary Catherine Bateson's *Composing a Life*. It was late and she couldn't sleep. Her husband, Michael, lay beside her, snoring loudly, oblivious to her insomnia. She looked over at him, seeing their darling ten-year-old daughter in his full lips and finely carved nose – mementos of her face in his. Her thoughts oddly careened to her life without them, and she shuddered. Why do her thoughts overpower her that way? So pessimistic and suspicious, those annoying thoughts. She shook her head for clarity and returned to reading.

Bateson's words spoke directly to her. 'Because women were traditionally taught to emphasize service, their choices may be unintelligible and therefore deeply suspect. I have been struck by how terribly hard women worked as students and later on in their careers, and how often work is unappreciated when the motive behind it is not understood. Women were worn down or burnt out' (Bateson, 1989). Tess thought immediately of the dietetics profession and how the experience of burnout was prevalent for her and her colleagues. She wondered how much the experience of burnout contributed to some of her most creative and intelligent dietetic colleagues deciding to leave the profession. Her thoughts returned to one of her friends, Gabrielle. They used to work together at a downtown hospital. During a recent chat at a networking event, Gabi mentioned that her work was getting more difficult. There was conflict between the dietitians and the managers about needing to justify the services that dietitians provided. More recently, Gabi was struggling with being asked to do research on the effectiveness of a weight-loss drug – research sponsored using money from the drug's manufacturer. Gabi, usually upbeat and positive, seemed downtrodden. It astounded Tess to hear Gabi talk about leaving dietetics. Tess decided that her next class with the dietetic undergrads would be a good time to raise this topic of professional burnout and ask them what they could do to prevent such an occurrence as a way of sustaining the profession. She could share a story with them of an imaginary dietitian that had a breakdown mid-career and decided to leave the profession. She'd give Gabi a pseudonym. Amy. She decided to phone Gabi tomorrow and get her permission to adapt the classroom story from her own life. She thought it would probably be a composite life, a combination of Gabi's story with that of others. She began to think of the abundance of stories told to her by real women, her dietitian colleagues struggling to keep their professional lives together. Life imitating art, art imitating life. She was excited by this idea and that anticipation made sleep even more elusive. She continued reading, composing her life.

Chapter Three – Secret Discontent

Week 3: September 21

'Hello everyone. Please take your seats. I have a story to tell you and I need your advice.' Tess decided to leave the discussion of that day's articles for later. The students assembled themselves, disciplined in rows of desks, their eyes on Tess as she disrupted them once again from the usual way to start a class. Stories aren't often, if ever, presented as pedagogical tools for dietetic practice. What would she think of next?

'OK, I want to tell you about Amy. She has worked in a hospital for seven years as a dietitian, not long. She started out as casual, taking shifts in surgery, diabetes, outpatients, and medicine. We met for tea recently, and she's having a really hard time at work. She gave me permission to share her story with you as a way to prepare you for the realities of your chosen career. Remember when I mentioned during our first class about the notion of the promise of professionalism?' Several heads nodded in recollection. 'As I share this story with you, I would like you to think about two things: What is the promise of professionalism, and how might you support Amy in her current situation? Are you ready for Amy's story?'

Feet shuffled, bodies stirred, but all eyes were trained in normalizing ways on Tess. They were ready.

'Amy is not happy at work. She spends most of her day in a cardiovascular rehab program, working with people who have recently had heart attacks, counselling them on what's called heart-healthy eating. She believes strongly in a health-centred approach compared to a weight-centred approach. This means her philosophy is based on the science that says you don't necessarily have to lose weight to be healthy – that it's more about being active and nourishing yourself with a variety of foods. Who here has heard about the health-centred approach?'

Tess noticed quite a few hands go up. 'Oh! How did you hear about it?'

'My friend is in human kinetics and they had a guest lecture by Jacqui Gingras, I think she's coming to our class later this term. Anyway, she told me that Jacqui was coming to talk to their class and I decided to go, too. I was a bit surprised that I hadn't heard anything about that in our program, and Jacqui was pretty pumped about it. Someone even said she was too biased, you know. Anyway …'

'Well, she certainly does hold her views very strongly, but she doesn't come by those beliefs frivolously. She makes a sound judgment based on the evidence. Just like Amy, actually.' Tess was slightly amused by this student's assessment of Jacqui's seminar. She would pass it on when they met later.

'OK, back to Amy, who is incredibly diligent with the evidence, believes strongly that dietitians need an arsenal of evidence, as she puts it, to be respected in our current health care environment. So she makes a practice of scouring the literature for evidence to support the health-centred model, and she found a great deal of evidence. So you might think, "Great! She has the evidence, she promotes this with her boss, the medical director of the cardiac program, and they all start working from this philosophy." Wrong.' Tess paused with a sip of her tea and quickly assessed where the students were with her story. Convinced they were present, she continued.

'So, she brings in a stack of journal articles, I mean like fifty or so articles, and puts them on her director's desk, a highly qualified physician, and begins to share with her what she has learned. "We need to stop promoting weight loss and start promoting metabolic fitness," she says. The doctor disagrees. Amy says, "We both took an oath to do no harm and there is harm when you promote only weight loss, and it is also harmful to the core of your being."' Tess remembered those exact words told to her by Gabi. She remembered the look of astonishment on Gabi's face when she shared with Tess the story of the physician who simply crossed her arms and asked, incredulously, 'Are you trying to tell me that I should not be encouraging my patients to lose weight?' Tess remembered the knot growing in her stomach as Gabi's story unfolded. Tess had never liked conflict, and Gabi's exchange with the physician was almost too much to bear. Although she hadn't been there, the story was written on Tess's body, scribed into her gut.

'Did I mention that Amy is one courageous, persevering woman?' The students laughed, already knowing that to question the long-standing practices of a senior physician was a risky endeavour. Tess vaguely wondered how they learned this, how they 'got' the joke. She realized that this knowledge for these students was social capital – they got further when they knew who had power in society, in medical hierarchies. They were smart, perceptive women. Had the dietetic curriculum reinforced this knowledge? Tess made yet another mental note to ask Jacqui.

'Amy is not deterred by the director's disbelief. She invites her to look at the evidence, to look past the fact that large people don't conform to society's ideal. The evidence tells us we are not good at promoting weight loss – and not only are we not good at it, we make people worse. She asserts that the practice would never be acceptable in any other medical situation. So, Amy tells me that the director just could not change her approach. She insists on promoting weight loss because she believes that if her patients lose weight, they will get better. To this claim Amy responds – and I love this part – "You're assuming that if people have more reasons than anyone else to lose weight, they are going to be more successful and that's just not what the evidence supports." Amy tells me that the patients the physician refers to her for weight-loss counselling feel so guilty. They say, "My doctor tells me if I don't lose weight, I'm going to have another heart attack or stroke." Fear does not work. So Amy and the medical director have a fundamental difference of professional opinion. Now, the plot thickens. Recently, the cardiac program accepted funding from Roche, producers of Xenical, to conduct research on whether taking Xencial to lose weight helps reduce risk of cardiac problems. OK, let me stop for a moment. Who can tell me about Xenical?'

The line of story-telling monologue was broken, and it took a moment for the students to adjust to the shift. 'Uh, yeah, isn't that the fat-blocking drug that prevents fat from being absorbed so the total number of calories is less because the fat goes right through?' offered Marci.

'Yes, precisely. Marci, thank you for that. And what are the physical side effects to such a drug?' Tess wanted to expose more of the story.

Marci responded again, 'Well, uh, it's kinda nasty. Um, what do they call it, uh, anal leakage, fecal urgency, liquid stools. That's gross!' She laughed nervously along with other students who were not yet comfortable with such graphic bowel talk, the purview of clinical dietetic practice.

'Yeah, that's definitely gross. And did you know that the drug, Xenical, was tested for only two years before it was approved for use in Canada? As a dietitian, what would you need to counsel someone to add to their diet if they were taking Xenical?'

Well, they'd have to take extra fat-soluble vitamins to replace what is not absorbed because the fat is not absorbed.' It was clear Marci had done some extra reading on the topic of weight-loss pharmaceuticals.

'By a show of hands, how many of you would expect Amy to be against the research funded by Roche?'

The entire class put up their hands.

'Right you are. It's sort of a no-brainer, isn't it? So, in addition to Amy's boss continuing to promote weight loss and insisting that Amy advise these patients on how to lower their caloric intake to lose weight, Amy is being told she must counsel the research participants on how to eat healthily while they are in the study. It's a double-blind controlled study, so Amy and the participants don't actually know who is getting the Xenical or a placebo. OK. So, obviously on many levels, Amy feels caught in a highly contentious ethical dilemma. She doesn't want to go to work anymore. She is stressed to the max. She has started having nightmares, she does all kinds of things to delay going to bed, she has a chronic migraine and aching back, and she is increasingly cynical about the kind of work she is doing and is capable of doing. Now, this is where you come in. What do you think she should do? What kind of advice do you have for Amy? What can you say to her to prevent her from leaving the profession or leaving the job. I want you to start with some basic ideas. Write down your immediate thoughts, make some notes, and spend some time over the next week thinking about your response. Also, use the readings from Travers, Austin, and DeVault. You will have to read ahead for DeVault, but she speaks specifically to this situation of inner conflict. I will expect you to hand in a one-page explanation about your advice to Amy at the start of next class. I'll count it as one of your reader responses. And, since we aren't going to have time to talk about Austin's article today, we'll start there next time.

Tess noticed a couple of students who needed to ask her for more information. 'Does anyone have any questions?'

Candice asked, 'Does Amy have kids?'

'No.'

Dani asked, 'Does she have any other job prospects?'

'No, not currently, but do you think maybe she should start looking?' Tess smiled and, surprisingly, Dani smiled back. Her question was facetious and didn't reflect the seriousness that her story implied. She tried to redress her sarcastic humour. 'Remember, there are consequences to leaving a hospital position. You lose your seniority, your benefits, and your holiday pay. And there aren't that many jobs in clinical dietetics at the moment. So, think carefully if you're feeling compelled to encourage Amy to abandon the entire enterprise. Put yourselves in Amy's place at this stage of her career. What I mean by that is, consider the promise of dietetics, whatever you imagine that to be for you at this time in your life, in your education, and your familiarity with the profession. Put yourself in Amy's situation. Consider the big picture as much as you can.'

Tess paused again. The students took her up on her advice to make some notes and began to pack up their belongings. She finished a little early and had put them a week behind in their readings, but she hoped it wasn't in vain. She hoped that story telling about issues of professional conflict would help the students in the long run.

ᔦ▪

Jacqui was at home, doing dishes again. There was no end to household chores when a baby arrived. What was it about a baby that made household chores so unrelenting? The phone rang, and Jacqui quickly stripped off her yellow gloves to answer it, a welcomed distraction. It was Ariana.

'Hi, Jacqui. I just came across this article and had to phone you immediately.' Ariana sounded a bit breathless.

'Wow, I thought I was the only one who got that excited about journal articles. What's it about?'

'It is from nursing, of course. They have done so much wonderful writing on the process and theory of nursing practice. I wish dietetics had such a voluminous pool of literature to draw from, but, as it is, we go to the nurses.'

'Yeah, I attribute it to the large number of nurses compared to dietitians, but I think it might be more than just numbers. There seems to be a culture of inquiry present in nursing that is completely absent in dietetics. We need to change that. Really, only one dietetic journal in Canada!'

Ariana could barely contain herself, 'I know and this article is so wicked and disruptive! It talks about nurse-on-nurse aggression. Nurse-on-nurse aggression, can you believe it? I thought of you instantly because of what you told me is coming up in your research about competition between dietitians. And in the article they point to nursing undergraduate education as – let me find it here – "one of the mechanisms that reinforces this position," and I believe the author is referring here to medical hegemony, uncritical acceptance of dominant groups within health care.'

'How interesting. That's great. Hey, if the nurses feel oppressed, what do dietitians feel even further down the medical hierarchy? What's the reference? I clearly need to read this article. Maybe Tess would like to include it in her syllabus.'

'I'll email you an electronic version. It's by Freshwater (Freshwater, 2000). There's one more bit I want to read to you, I just love it: "If the education is controlled by the powerful and limited to the curricula that support their values, little conflict occurs. However, it would seem that conflict does occur, although not necessarily overtly. The conflict that arises manifests itself in other ways, often as internalized self-deprecation, self-harm and horizontal violence." Isn't that provocative?'

'It sure is. I can't wait to read it. Thanks so much, Ariana. It feels good to know that you're looking out for the juicy theory for my dissertation – my sister dietetic theorist!'

'Oh, it's mutual, Jacqui. I should go. I know you are busy. Peg and I are just getting ready to head to the market. I love Saturday mornings with her.'

'I envy you. Evyn is napping right now, but we are just trying to keep our heads above water. Kelly has dropped off the laundry and I'm doing dishes. How dull!'

'Oh, but you have an incredible daughter you get to be with every morning. How decadent!'

'Yes, yes, you're right. She is very decadent. Talk to you soon.'

&

Gabrielle took a sip of her tea and nestled herself deep into the couch in Jacqui's office. She had been looking forward to the idea of supervision ever since receiving Jacqui's email last week. It wouldn't matter why she was coming to Jacqui's office, she loved the thought of sitting and talking over matters of dietetic practice with her colleagues, her friends. Gabrielle looked around the room at the women she so admired. Tess, glorious in aubergine, a graceful force in their profession. Ariana, a self-proclaimed dietetic theorist poet, her British accent only adding to her mystique and allure. Jacqui, activist, dietitian, therapist, and now mother – her heart swelling with joy in her latest subjectivity. Gabrielle loved these women and was blessed to have them in her life. This latest adventure of therapy together was a gift to know them better – a gift she was ready to embrace.

'Welcome, everyone!' Jacqui started. 'Shall we begin with a check in and then get on to the matter of supervision and how we want it to look?'

'Sounds good to me. I'll start.' Gabrielle made her eagerness known with her instant response. 'I'm just so happy to be here with you. Work has been really difficult, and I've been wondering again if I'm just not cut out for this job. Seven years I've been wondering! The timing for this group is perfect. I'm prepared to be inspired by you!' The women laughed, knowing that it was not a passive experience for Gabrielle, but a hearty, mutual festival of inspiration for all.

'OK, me next.' Ariana chimed in with her lyrical voice. 'This past week has been exceedingly trying. My good friend Jenny just passed away from breast cancer. It took her too fast. We're all devastated. The service was Sunday and I read some poetry for the occasion. It was incredibly hard. I'm emotionally battered at the moment. Not sure what use I'll be here today, but it is so comforting to be in your presence.' Ariana's tiny frame was weary, propped up in the corner of the couch next to Gabrielle. Her eyes said more about the despair of her friend's passing. There was momentary silence in the room as the women contemplated the gravity of Ariana's experience.

'It sounds awful, Ariana. How old was Jenny?'

'She was just 44. Such a fantastic person – funny, loyal. We used to run together, with grey geese chasing us down as we went through the park. I'll never forget those geese – totally wicked, those geese. I wrote a poem to remember our running together.'

'I would love to hear your poem. You don't by chance have it with you?'

'Well, I do. Jenny's sister wanted it printed on the, what would you call it, some kind of program for the memorial service. I have a copy here.'

Ariana reached into her bedraggled knapsack and pulled out a purple leather-bound journal. The way her hands caressed the smooth leather indicated her love of and tenderness towards the words that resided there. Inside she had carefully sheaved the leaflet. Gabi closed her eyes and leaned back as Ariana began to read.

'It's called "In Celebration."'

> *In celebration of the runner I am thundering in*
> *your ears*
>
> *In celebration of the runner I am racing through*
> *your veins*
>
> *In celebration of the runner I am pulsing from*
> *the day's full-blooded sun to ruddy up your*
> *gaunt cheeks*
>
> *In celebration of the runner I am stinging your*
> *eyes alive to the tone-still bliss-lone depths of the*
> *conifered forest*
>
> *In celebration of the runner*
> *I am matching your hatched sobs, tight chest anxious for*
> *spare air*
> *I am footloose among you*
> *I am pacing the hard parts*
> *I am throbbing on your temple*
> *I am the sweat of your furrowed brow*
> *my brine is the brine of the tears that runnel*
> *your renegade face*

I am just on your shoulder
I am coursing, cruising, cramping, leaping,

I charge you now to keep in step with all I relayed of
life's exhilaration
I give you simply
my strong willed heart
endurance
love.'

'That's beautiful, Ariana. I want your poetry to grace my funeral service. You're so incredibly gifted.' Jacqui was emphatic in her support for Ariana's work. She dreamed of her poetry daring to be as evocative.

'Thank you … everyone. I'm going to miss her so much. Such a beautiful spirit, that woman.' Ariana carefully, tenderly, replaced the leaflet in her journal. She wished someone else to speak.

There was another quiet pause as the women contemplated their luck at still being alive. Adriana's sharing had brought a new perspective to their consciousness.

'I feel we honour Jenny's memory by being here today and taking risks together. I sense she would have been so in favour of our gathering.' Tess, ever ready with language bridges and connections, shared her sentiment to the smiling nods of the three other women. 'As some of you know, I'm currently teaching an undergrad class of dietetic students and much has arisen already about my place in this profession and how we prepare new dietitians for their work. It has called everything into question again for me. I hope that I can share more as this group evolves, but I will leave it at that for now.'

'I guess it's my turn.' Jacqui didn't like being last. She felt burdened with having to carry and close the circle. 'I have great hopes for our work together. I need this time with you in so many ways. I've been working hard to finish my dissertation and applying for faculty jobs, and the emotions and stress and the tension are running very high.' She emphasized the word 'very,' but she hadn't really needed to, as the mere acknowledgement of emotion and tension was rare for Jacqui. 'Sometimes I feel like I just need to walk out of my office and keep on walking, not looking back, not stopping until I get home and can feel the loving arms of my baby girl around my neck. Evyn is pulling me home in every moment. I want to be there with her and Kelly all the time.' With these last words Jacqui's voice broke. She was surprised by this spilling of emotion and hadn't intended to cry, but the tears burst forward, insistent and hot on her cheeks. Sheepish, she looked down and started to sob. Tess hesitated then gently placed her hand on Jacqui's back, murmuring a soft encouragement to just allow the tears their place. Jacqui had no choice as she realized the enormous strain she had been managing the last few months.

'You and Kelly are taking on so much. It's totally understandable that you would feel overwhelmed, Jacq.' Gabrielle offered her support.

'Yeah, I know it's a lot and it will be much better when Kelly's term is over. She just has these last three classes to finish and then she graduates. That will be amazing – an incredible accomplishment for her and for our family. I'm so proud of her ...' The tears returned, but this time they were accompanied by a smile, her expression revealing more joy than sorrow. She realized she felt less overwhelmed by shifting the emphasis from her strain to Kelly's accomplishments. Tess, Gabrielle, and Ariana nodded sympathetically in a display of support, but also of relief in the shift in Jacqui's demeanour. It was sometimes difficult to know what to do and what to say in those moments.

'Oh, God! Get it together, woman!' Jacqui admonished herself as she sniffed and reached for a handful of Kleenex to blow her nose. 'This is not how I imagined starting our group together. I would like it if we could move on and talk about how we want our supervision to look.' Jacqui straightened her back and moved closer to the edge of her chair, obviously not wanting to get so comfortable again as to permit more outbursts. The other women adjusted themselves, too, falling into more familiar task-oriented roles.

'What do you think of having an actual therapist facilitate this for us?' Jacqui asked, setting a tone and a direction.

'Hmm, I never considered inviting a therapist in to our group. It would be a new experience for me. Do you have someone in mind?' Gabrielle had always been open to new perspectives, so her response was of no surprise to Jacqui.

'Yeah, I have a couple women in mind that I respect and admire as compassionate and skilled therapists. I believe they both have experience facilitating supervision for other counsellors. I could give them a call to see if they would be interested. What do you two think about that?'

Tess seemed pensive and hesitated. Ariana volunteered, 'I think the potential to get into some meaningful stuff would be there with a therapist facilitating the process. I'm game.' Ariana looked to Tess.

'How much would it cost us?' Tess asked.

'Yes, it will cost us something. I'm guessing around $100 to $150 a session, probably sessions will last an hour or an hour and a half. So for each of us, between 25 and 40 bucks.' Jacqui knew that Tess and Michael were struggling financially since he was laid off last fall. She reminded herself to be patient and gentle with Tess as they ventured into unfamiliar territory.

'That seems reasonable. I might even be able to get it covered through work if the therapist is a registered psychologist. That would be helpful.' Tess still had her part-time job at the cancer agency on the westside to rely on, although the work she was doing there was taking its toll. Tess shared with Jacqui recently that, although it was emotionally difficult to work with people who had cancer and were very likely to die, she found herself more demoralized by administrators who didn't understand or value her work and her desire to do qualitative research on the experience of living with changed health status. One of her bosses, whom she thought would be supportive of her starting a small project, said to her as he leaned back in his enormous leather chair, 'Look around, dear woman. You don't really think that qualitative research in nutrition is going to pull in the kind of money to build research facilities, hire scientists, and accumulate necessary technology, do you?' Clearly a redundant and highly patronizing question. It wasn't the first time Tess thought about leaving, but she didn't really feel she had a choice. The money was excellent and she needed that stability, especially with her daughter, Zoë, beginning to show more interest in equestrian. Riding lessons were expensive, but the wild joy on Zoë's face when she mounted those beautiful, enormous beasts was worth every penny. Tess realized she had wandered off in her thoughts as she heard Jacqui responding.

'One of them is registered. I will contact her first. Her name is Carly. So I will email you with the details when I hear back from her. Excellent! I'm really looking forward to seeing what happens.'

'Jacq, before we finish can you tell us a little bit more about what you think might happen?' Apparently Gabrielle's enthusiasm was also shaded by practicality. Tess and Ariana nodded in agreement with Gabrielle's question. They all wanted more information to set their minds at ease about the process.

'Well, from my experience with supervision when I worked at Wellspring a few years ago, the supervisor created a space for us to discuss issues of professional concern – so what was difficult or was challenging us in our work, which at the time was facilitating support groups for women who identified as struggling with eating and body image issues. In our group there was a male physician, a psychologist, a counsellor, and me. The supervisor, Lesley, came in the first time bringing several ordinary objects with her. If I remember correctly, she brought a wine glass, a little mouse ornament, a child's toy, a feather, a polished rock paperweight, and some other things. I think a candle, too. Anyway, she placed all these objects on a table in the middle of our circle and asked that we each pick an object that somehow spoke to our experience of our work in these support groups. So we took turns speaking to the association between the object we chose and our story. That was probably the best session we had with Lesley because, as you know, things blew up at Wellspring. Right around the same time that we started supervision, we found out that the physician had slept with one of his patients – and although he had been disciplined by his college, none of us really felt safe working with him in that capacity any longer. Actually, it was at our very next session together that all of this came out into the open. There was so much emotion and pain and trauma. We didn't give Lesley much of a chance to supervise us. We were a wounded group. So, OK, maybe that's not the best example of supervision!' Jacqui realized that her awful experience could ruin the possibility for a supportive and generative opportunity.

'Of course, our experience will be entirely different!'

'Of course!' Ariana exclaimed. 'I couldn't bear the thought of finding out you had a relationship with a client, Jacqui! Especially since you wrote that paper on trust. That would be shattering. If that's a premonition of what's to come, count me out!'

'OK, let me assure you I'm not sleeping with any of my clients and I never will. I wish I'd never mentioned that. What a fiasco!' Jacqui laughed nervously, regretting her unscripted rendition of a very trying time for her professionally. She had just finished her masters degree in Edmonton and returned to Vancouver to set up her practice. Not four months later she found herself embroiled in a thorny ethical debacle. She was attempting to compose a life imbued by integrity, honest hard work, and the truth of her conviction that by simply providing nutrition knowledge, her work as a dietitian was incomplete. Her association with the physician in question became untenable. She chose to leave even though she had worked hard to promote Wellspring and had been richly acknowledged for her efforts. One month, after a deluge of media attention intended to raise the community profile of Wellspring and, of course, Jacqui's own special brand of nutrition therapy, the physician offered her an all-expense-paid trip to Whistler including tickets for two to attend an opening gala, Crush, at Cornucopia, Whistler's renowned food and wine extravaganza. She accepted, taking along her lover at the time and having a magnificently decadent weekend – superior wines paired expertly with gorgeously plated delicacies, luscious desserts, port, dancing, white lights, rapturous sex. All of her senses imbibed with ecstatic abandon. On another level, the experience reinforced her understanding that if she worked hard, she would be rewarded. It was a heady time, leaving her filled most of all with a sense of her own power and a growing awareness of her unlimited appetite for more. All of these events culminated in the tortuous decision to leave Wellspring. But it was, for her, the right decision, and she never looked back.

ε▲

Tess leaned across the passenger seat of her modest Toyota Corolla and picked up her ringing cell phone. She checked the number before answering, a habit she acquired from being on a casual list early on in her career. It was Zoë calling from home. 'Hello darling. What's up?'

'Mom, can Ben and Julia come over for a movie tonight? We've already checked with their parents and with Dad and they said it's OK. Please, Mom.'

Zoë was thorough for a ten-year old. 'What time?'

'Well, we could get a pizza and then start the movie. 7:00?'

Tess became aware she shouldn't be talking on the phone and driving at the same time when she heard a honk from the driver behind her. The light had turned green. 'Oh, give me a break!'

'Mom, come on! Why not?' Zoë thought Tess was talking to her and had instantly become defensive. Tess noticed this becoming more and more of an immediate response with Zoë. Did this increasing seriousness and defiance signal impending teen rebellion? Tess mourned the passing of Zoë's more light-hearted and easy-going behaviour.

'No, Zoë, not you. Oh, God! Sorry, sweetheart. I was talking to another driver.'

'Well, what's the point, Mom? They can't hear you.'

'Yeah, thanks, Zoë. I never thought of that! What movie are you planning on getting? Will Dad be home?'

'Yes, Mom, I've already checked with Dad. I just told you that. Geez, Mom, pay attention. Maybe you shouldn't be driving and talking at the same time.'

'Zoë, so full of brilliant ideas today, aren't you? The movie party sounds great. Save me a piece of pizza, OK? And, what movie are you getting?'

'Cool. Thanks, Mom. See ya!' Tess heard Zoë yell to her friends even before hanging up. She desperately missed time with her daughter and husband when she had to work late, and now it seemed like they were picking up the pieces in her absence. She began to wonder why Zoë didn't tell her what movie they were watching. She was deep in thought about her family, resenting the intrusion of work into her relationship with her two favourite people, when her phone rang again. The sound jarred her, and she yelled 'Oh, for god's sake, leave me alone!' before again reaching across the seat for the phone.

It was Jacqui that time. 'Hey, Tess. How's it going?' She sounded relaxed, with time to spare. Tess didn't have the same luxury.

'I'm not doing too well right at the moment. I just screamed at another driver and then again at the phone. I'm running late for my shift at the cancer agency. All this driving is going to be the death of me.' Tess didn't intend to unload her tension on Jacqui. It just happened.

Jacqui didn't want to contribute further to Tess's feeling of harassment, so she got to the point. 'I hear ya. I know you are incredibly busy, but something just happened and I would really like to get your advice about what I should do. Maybe we could meet again for tea after your class on Tuesday.' There was a brief pause, which Jacqui interpreted as Tess attempting to find a way to decline. 'Only for fifteen or twenty minutes. I would really appreciate it, Tess.'

'Yeah, sure, yeah, sorry. I was just kinda distracted. Oh, God, I should really pull over. This is getting ridiculous!'

'No, no, that's OK, Tess. Let's talk later. I'll call you tomorrow while Evyn is napping, say late morning.'

'Oh, that would be great. And, yes, let's meet on Wednesday. I will need to debrief about the class, so that will be perfect. Same place?'

'Yes, same place. Great! Thanks, Tess. Drive safe.' Jacqui was immensely relieved to be able to connect with someone about a response she received on an article she submitted to the Dietitians of Canada (DC) *Journal of Dietetic Practice and Research*, an incident that had her once again wondering what to do.

&a.

In the Canadian dietetics profession, Jacqui was known as a bit of a troublemaker, or what poststructural educational theorist Patti Lather called, an 'outsider-within' (Lather, 1991). With tenacity and zeal she had taken up the issue of her professional organization's acceptance of funding from pharmaceutical companies that promoted drugs for weight loss. Her activist inclinations had elicited a variety of (non)responses from the organization, ranging from 'You are the only one to have indicated a concern' to the latest 'Your paper is too opinionated and we have decided not to send it out for further review.' These responses highlighted the absolute inertia of organizational change and only fuelled Jacqui's desire for more elaborate and sustained actions.

During a 2003 summer course on the hermeneutics of pedagogy with Drs. Munir Vellani and Karen Meyer, Jacqui wrote a paper on the issue of trust, exploring it from the standpoint of educational and relational theory. She claimed that nutrition counsellors couldn't be trusted if the organization to which they belong were engaged in activities that constituted a conflict of interest. In the paper she named the organization that she felt was compromising the interests of the profession and of the people dietitians were supposed to serve through its relationship with pharmaceutical companies – and she named the companies as well. Having pursued other venues for change, she had abandoned tact and spoke directly to the issues, unrepentant. Given the nature of the topic and the specificity to Canadian dietitians, she considered it a relevant article for submission to the *Canadian Journal for Dietetic Practice and Research*. She was wrong.

Several weeks after submitting the article, she received an email from the editor stating that her article was not suitable for publication and, thus, had not been sent to reviewers. Jacqui was stunned by this foreclosing of professional debate, what she considered an act of gate keeping by the editor. After a few weeks of reflecting on the implications of the rejection, Jacqui emailed the editor and asked her to elaborate on what it was about the paper that precluded it from anonymous peer review. It was as if the editor had been awaiting the invitation to say more. What followed was a lengthy and detailed response to the article's transgressions and failures. The article was too personal. It referenced too many sources. It was too long and too difficult to read. It lacked an explicit concluding 'relevance-to-practice' section. For these reasons, and more, the editor felt justified in returning the manuscript, without review.

The process stung Jacqui immeasurably. She found the editor's remarks contradictory and largely baseless. She wanted to share them with Tess. Jacqui needed to reconcile her repeated attempts to initiate change with the continued obstructions manifested by people in the organization. She needed advice on how to proceed.

Chapter Four – Skittering Times

We live in skittering times, when the old reliables
of our own invention are beginning to crack.

(Jardine, 1998, p. 135)

Week 4: September 28

Dani walked in the back door to the classroom just in time to get the last seat at the back. Her last-minute arrival was becoming routine, hard to break. Tess was writing on the board. Three words: consumerism, commodification, complicit. She finished writing, her script large and fluid across the board, and then she turned towards the students.

'Good morning. OK, we need some time at the end of class to talk about your first assignment and we need time to talk about S. Bryn Austin's paper. Is there anything else to add to today's agenda?' Tess looked around the class while taking a drink of her latte. Meg put up her hand and Tess abbreviated her sip, with a nod to Meg to speak.

'Yeah, have you got the Blackboard glossary thing set up? I haven't been able to find it.' Meg was one of the few students who had even considered looking for the glossary. She was highly motivated to do well in the class, feeling the need to impress Tess since hearing her comments about Meg's work on the eastside.

'Right, thanks for reminding me. I've asked someone to get that set up for me with a function that permits each of us to add words and phrases to our glossary. It should be finished by this afternoon. I hope. Again, my intention with the glossary is to help us acquire the language to read these papers. OK, so speaking of the papers, I would like to hear from each of you one word that describes your response to Austin's paper. Pull out your copy of the chapter and take a moment and when you are ready, start us off. One word.' Tess gestured to the front of the class, to the student who sat on Tess's far right.

After a couple of minutes of paper shuffling, chairs scratching the floor, whispered remarks, came quiet. One by one, a stream of words surfaced.

'Complicated. Dense. Difficult. Challenging. Uh, confusing. Interesting. Twisted. Um, exposing. Jargony. Amazing. Random. Exaggerated. Unbelievable. Distorted. Deceptive. Misleading. Pretentious. Intriguing. Incredible. Weird. Um, excessive. Alarmist. Bloated. Brilliant.' Tess looked to Dani who would be the last to speak. 'Brutal.' Dani's eyes met Tess's, conveying clearly her disdain for the second week in a row.

'Uh, OK, great. Great words. One question, what is meant by "random?"'

Marci responded, 'Yeah, I mean like strange or weird, like totally unexpected. Like, I found the article came out of the blue, you know.'

A small smile played across Tess's face as she watched several other students nod in agreement with the explanation.

'Alright then. I get it. You loved the article and you want more of the same!' The tension broke with Tess's laughter and that of many of the young women.

'I promise you, the reading shifts a little after this week, but in the meantime, let's get into Austin's premise or thesis for this chapter, which is … anyone?' Tess waited.

'The whole desire and restraint thing was pretty interesting, for sure. I've never thought of low-fat yogurt quite like that before, but more from a health perspective, not economics.' Meg was quick to fill the quiet spaces.

'Yes, it's a clever analysis of the diet food industry. I would suggest that the thesis, Austin's main concept, her argument, is directly associated with the example you gave, Meg. What do others think?'

'I think what she's getting at is that the food industry can create a food product based on health claims and then convince nutritionists to help market that product. She kinda makes the nutritionists out to be sorta dumb. What's the word … yeah, she makes them into unwitting accomplices of the diet industry.' Dani's contribution was right on the mark.

'Yes, Dani. So consumers interested in choosing healthy foods need to acquire a discourse – there's that word again – a nutrition discourse, so they can understand what 'low-fat' actually means and they can therefore choose foods that nutritionists have told them are healthy. They wouldn't buy low-fat foods if the nutritionists and the marketers hadn't told them low-fat was beneficial for their health. Now, a momentary aside. Who has read Gary Taubes's article in *Science* called "The Soft Science of Dietary Fat" (Taubes, 2001)? I highly recommend it to all of you. I will put a PDF version on Blackboard for you if you have a moment, but it won't be part of the official course reading, if you know what I mean.' The students glanced at each other and smiled at Tess's innuendo. 'The point I'm attempting to make here is that the ubiquitous low-fat-equal-healthy-eating message has a sordid history. Austin goes so far as to say that "the insistence on specific values … does invoke the assumed authority of scientific precision in a situation where there is none." And "the stalking of dietary fat in public health promotion has been pursued with a zeal well beyond that justified by the field's own scientific research." I want you to really think about what that means for you as nutrition professionals. You need to know that the low-fat health-promotion message arose more out of politics and economics than out of what we claim as value-neutral scientific evidence. The story with low-fat foods produced by the diet industry is similar. We'd like to believe that low-fat is about benefiting populations, but it is also benefiting corporations in colossal ways. This is significant.'

Tess took a break to take in a little more caffeine and to give the students a moment to consider what she was saying. She also heard herself sounding slightly presumptuous, to borrow from how a student described Austin's article. Tess knew the dangers of lecturing. She needed to step back and find a way to encourage the students to engage their own imagination.

'OK, these words that I have up on the board. Why do you think I chose these words as key to this article? Take three minutes and write or draw what you see are the connections between the words as they relate to what Austin has written.'

When three minutes were up, Candice asked Tess if she could share a drawing of how the words interrelated. Tess enthusiastically invited her to the front of the class to reproduce her drawing on the board. Candice drew two circles, interconnected. Inside each circle, she wrote the words 'consumerism' and 'health promotion;' one in each circle. In the space where the two circles intersected, she neatly wrote 'commodification of health.'

'Oh, how very clever! Could you share with us a few remarks of explanation for such a rendering?' Tess was genuinely impressed with this students' graphic representation and wished more students would offer such visual responses to the text. Perhaps in time.

Candice obliged. 'Well, the way I understand what this Austin person is trying to say is when consumerism meets health promotion, health is commodified. You can't have commodification without consumerism.'

'Uh-huh. Does anyone have another interpretation or questions?' Tess was interested in having the students interact more with each other.

'Yeah, so where would you put the word "complicit?"' Dani desired completion, thoroughness.

'Um ... OK. What about this?' Candice added to her drawing with a flourish.

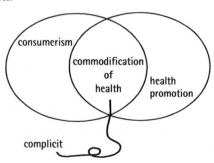

'You are complicit if you participate in the commodification of health,' Candice stated intrepidly.

'So, if I recommend to someone to eat low-fat so they reduce their risk of heart disease, diabetes, cancer, I'm complicit? Is that what you are saying?' Dani had taken exception to how Austin had labelled a majority of the nutrition profession. Her worldview was threatened. Tess remained quiet.

'Well, yeah, that's the point of the article. It was Austin's idea, not mine, Dani.' Candice put down the chalk and took her seat, determined not to further engage Dani and sounding a little annoyed at Dani's question.

'Well, we can still promote low-fat foods that aren't produced by the diet industry, right? We're not complicit then, right? I don't even believe in dieting, but I do believe in healthy eating.' Dani compromised.

'I've started to think that what we call healthy eating is really just dieting and that we are trying to convince ourselves that we don't promote diets, but we do. If *diet* didn't have such a bad rap, we would just use the word, *diet*. Look, our name has the word right there – *dietitians*.' Meg had named the predicament that dietitians found themselves in when attempting to promote their work and their profession when *diet* was considered at cross-purposes to efforts of health promotion and disease prevention.

'"Conditions of consciousness" – that's the phrase in Austin's article,' Meg said as she continued to draw together her textual arsenal and her argument gathered momentum. She clutched her exorbitantly highlighted chapter in her fist. Tess almost expected her to start waving it as a manifesto might be brandished at a political rally. 'Consumers wouldn't even know about low-calorie, low-salt, low-fat foods if dietitians and nutritionists hadn't used social marketing to spread the word. This really frustrates me because I work with people who don't have access to enough food, and they hear that they shouldn't eat too much of this and too much of that, and it's maddening because it confuses and complicates their lives even more. I think it's about time that someone told the truth about how our actions do not always contribute to the big picture. Like Austin says, uh … yeah, right here, page 166, "Critics have pointed out the tendency to decontextualize health, ignoring significant social and economic forces shaping patterns of risk, and to focus instead on individual responsibility." I believe that not everyone has the same choices when it comes to their health. So what are we doing? What are we going to do?'

This question stopped the discussion cold: students were becoming somewhat aware of their predicament and their belatedness in coming to this state of questioning their field. They were making decisions about how to act or even whether to act. Tess remembered vaguely something Jacqui told her about Hannah Arendt. She would have to ask her about what action was possible in the students' increasing consciousness of their own situation (Levinson, 2001). She intuited that this was the moment of either action or paralysis for her students. She decided it was time for her to speak. The class would end in five minutes.

'OK. This has been an incredible discussion inspired by Austin's wildly dense, complicated article. Random. I like that word you used earlier. Random. Chaotic and random.' Tess stared for a brief moment out the window and murmured, 'It's all chaotic and random,' then snapping out of her reverie, returned her focus to the students. 'OK, please take out a piece of paper and write on the top of the page, "Somewhere a dietitian is not complicit …"' Tess turned to the board, erased her three words, but not Candice's diagram, and wrote the phrase in her signature script.

'I would like you to imagine – no, draft a manifesto for a dietitian professional who chooses not to be complicit. What is her practice like? Who does she associate with? What kind of work does she do? Of course, this will require you to define what you mean by complicit, and, of course, there may be differences in each of our definitions. I would like us to start our next class by sharing these responses and then, as usual, I would like you to hand them in to me. And, yes, I have your last responses here for you to pick up when you leave.' Immediately, the students took Tess's cue and began to pack up. 'Don't forget to prepare for your discussion on Liquori's article, and we will for sure talk about the first assignment, which is due the week after next. I hope all of you will have at least connected with a practising dietitian in the community – it doesn't matter what area of practice – and set up a time for a brief conversation about their work. I will be happy to answer any of your questions. Until then …'

With that the students gathered themselves and moved quickly on to their next obligations. Tess collected her papers, erased the board, and then found a chair to sit down in. She was exhilarated and exhausted. Things were moving so fast.

ॐ

Several members of Jacqui's academic community were gathered in a small seminar room to hear a well-established professor from their faculty talk about their doctoral degrees as vocational training. He described a twenty-four-month doctorate as the most efficient route to that first job:

September–April:	Take six courses, introduce yourself to faculty, read widely, write papers, submit manuscripts for publication
May to July:	Write comprehensive exams
August:	Write research proposal
September–June:	Defend comps and proposal, submit comp papers for publication, begin researching and writing, apply and interview for academic positions
July:	Defend dissertation, submit manuscripts for publication

September: Start in first academic position

When he suggested that students do their research by day and their analysis and writing by night, Jacqui laughed a little too long and too loud. Who was teaching the courses? Who was raising the children? Who was organizing the political rallies? Jacqui quickly realized that he wasn't trying to be funny. She was socialized by his stare, trained by the deeply puzzled look he gave her over the rim of his glasses. She realized that her experience of being a doctoral student was vastly different from what he envisioned, and she began to wonder about student lives as decontextualized and unencumbered. She didn't know many students who fit his description. Perhaps the vision of the twenty-four-month doctorate was unrealistic, unattainable. Given the dismal completion rate of doctoral students in their faculty, perhaps his vision of the twenty-four-month doctorate was actually a barrier to some who perceive the expectations as impossible or blamed themselves for not being able to get through.

Jacqui was reminded of other conversations with peers about alternative ways of being in research and how they luxuriated in the throng of potentials that unfolded when, to borrow from Emily Dickinson, *the possible's slow fuse is lit, by the Imagination*. These were the conversations that sustained her, that energized and uplifted, prepared her to face her computer screen each day, refreshed and excited about her work. These conversations were probably absent from the twenty-four-month doctorate – indeed, their presence probably required and resulted in a more realistic, more human, forty-eight-month program. These were the conversations that ignited her passion for academic life and that gave her hope for a different future. These were vitally important conversations: she might not have gotten through if it weren't for those conversations with brilliant, provocative peers from her academic community.

But for every such interaction with sympathetic peers, there was a reminder that not everyone was going to be receptive to her ideas. On the occasion of a peer editing activity, her work, her own academic writing, was judged as unreadable, dense, and theoretically incomprehensible. Jacqui sat alone in her office one day after receiving a barrage of strongly critical comments about an article that she was writing for her dissertation, work she thought had already been made more palatable through a series of merciless edits. 'It's too confusing. I did not understand any of it. Perhaps you should write an introductory paper to explain these ideas first,' her dietetic colleagues intoned. It seemed that there were times in the academy when scholars exhibited an unwillingness to extend knowledge, a judgment of what counts as knowledge, and a fierce defending of existing knowledge boundaries. She felt uneasy as the sharp edges of those boundaries pushed up against her body like a jagged knife, threatening to slice her open. She responded to her peers' comments with a nod and a smile while her thoughts whirled in antithesis. 'No, I refuse to simplify this work further. We must step out of our comfort zone. We must contend with new possibilities. Don't talk about my work this way.' It seemed she was trying to protect her writing like a mother might protect a defenceless child. The work was not defenceless, though. It spoke for itself. She remembered what Ronald Pelias said about the process of peer review in a book chapter he had co-authored with Elyse Pineau: 'Insiders believe they can write your article better than you can. They enjoy telling you this at regular intervals. Outsiders do not understand what you have written. They also enjoy telling you this. You listen. Sometimes it is very helpful. You do not enjoy it' (Pelias, 2004, p. 125). Jacqui attempted to protect herself, her desire for recognition, her belief that all had not yet been done. She thought about what Claudia Mills said about writers not deliberately seeking out difficult, stormy, heart-wrenching relationships in order to write about them, but finding themselves in these situations and writing their way out of the pain and perplexity (Mills, 2004, p. 103). 'I appreciate your comments' was all she could say.

As she was reconsidering her text, Judith Butler's words flooded her consciousness. *While we continue to try to change the world, we remain deeply tied by desire and the need for recognition to the world as it is* (Butler, 1999c). Jacqui's hurt was in response to feeling that knife edge, knowing panic, the fear of being different, marked as deviant, pretending not to care, and still continuing to desire sameness, to be made visible to those deranging her ideas, to have her writing and her work seen by them. Jacqui knew much of her reaction was tied to her own contradictory belief, however deeply buried inside her, that what she was doing was inappropriate. That her work couldn't endure the impossible standards she set even for herself. While Jacqui wrestled with affiliation, with having to make the untenable choice between comprehension and transgression, she heard in the far distance, a voice that offered respite, a solitary voice that urged her, 'Your work matters. I learned something. Keep writing.' Despite that plaintive voice encouraging her onward, Jacqui spent the rest of the day in the bookstore drinking coffee, eating brownies, and reading fashion magazines, desperate to comfort herself, desperate to escape.

ଈ

'Ariana! Hi! Oh, my goodness, this is a surprise. I wasn't expecting you. Come in.' Jacqui enthusiastically greeted Ariana at her door with a warm embrace.

'Well, you know, I was in the neighbourhood, as they say. Are you busy?'

'Uh, no, not really. I mean, yeah, I'm working on my writing. I seem to get good spurts while Evyn sleeps. Kelly is doing laundry. I don't think I'll ever not be busy again. Come in. I'll make some tea.'

Ariana wondered if she shouldn't intrude, but having just talked with Tess last night, she was a little concerned about Jacqui's emotional state and wanted to offer some support, even if it did interrupt the writing process.

'Tea would be lovely.' Ariana stepped into the living room, littered with toys of every possible type.

'Oh, God, excuse this mess! I just can't keep up with that girl. Every night I put the toys away and every morning, well, you can see what happens. My perfectionist tendencies are taking a beating. Do you think it's time to just give in?'

'My parents were the type who never let me play with any abandon in the house, so I think you should let her run wild. Who cares? Really, is there enough time in the day for all of it and what are you teaching her when she comes downstairs every morning to see it all clean? That's just setting an unreal expectation.'

'Hmm, maybe. I do know that I'm driving myself crazy trying to live the delusion that I can do it all. I don't want to do it all anymore. It is exhausting.' Jacqui filled the kettle and turned on the stove before she pulled up a chair to join Ariana at the kitchen table.

Ariana took a seat and noticed the piles of paper that covered Jacqui's computer desk. It filled her with tension knowing what it all represented – hours and hours of intellectual and emotional labour. It was no wonder Jacqui broke down during their meeting a few weeks ago. Jacqui noticed Ariana staring at her desk and immediately felt self-conscious. It had been Jacqui's mantra, professionally and personally, that finding balance in life was a healing endeavour. Noticing Ariana's appraisal of her desk and her deep involvement in her dissertation brought up unwelcome feelings of vulnerability.

'I'm a little worried about you, Jacq. What are you doing to take care of yourself these days?' Ariana got right to the point.

'Uh, yeah, not much. Some walking with Evyn in her stroller, but it's been really hard lately. Life has become just a little chaotic.'

'Yeah, seems that way. I am truly concerned. I spoke with Tess about it last night.'

'Oh, great. And what did she have to say?' Jacqui looked down, sheepish.

'Not too much. Her life is pretty intense right now, too. It's not healthy. Maybe she's projecting her imbalance onto you, but it doesn't matter. I'm worried that you are going to make real on your promise to leave dietetics, and that would be upsetting.'

'Well, if that's why you're here, I guess I better not tell you what happened at school yesterday. Just one more reason to abandon the whole enterprise. It just feels like I'm smashing my head against a wall. Why do I do it? Why am I so invested in dietetics? Why do I bother?'

The kettle began to whistle, and Jacqui noisily pushed her chair back across the tiled floor. She felt confrontational, exposed in her emotions. Ariana didn't respond, sensing a moment of quiet was necessary. Jacqui silently, deep in her thoughts, put together a pot of tea and placed it with two cups on the table. She turned away, retrieved the milk and the sugar bowl, and then sat down, this time making an attempt to lift her chair. Quietly.

'Ariana, yesterday I made a pledge to myself. I made a promise to stop smashing my head against that particular wall. I will not keep doing it.'

'I understand,' Ariana said in a very soft voice, a voice that was underpinned by determination and resolve. 'I've been thinking that, too. You mustn't leave the profession, though. The profession needs you.'

'Oh, that is very kind and encouraging, Ariana, but sometimes, lots of times, I feel very alone and unsupported in my work. That's what I'm really tired of, that feeling of being different, deviant. Deviant dietitian. Do you think we should start a Deviant Dietitians of Canada Network?' Jacqui was only partly kidding.

Ariana smiled at Jacqui's response. She was familiar with her friend's habit of using humour to distract people from her vulnerability, but Ariana was determined to discuss the underlying problem. Her tone remained earnest. 'Jacq, what happened yesterday?'

As Jacqui shared her experience with the peer editing process, Ariana sipped her hot tea and said nothing, she just listened and occasionally nodded. Finally, when she detected that Jacqui was nearing the end of her story, Ariana suggested, 'What about turning the gaze back on to the dietetic profession itself by publishing outside of dietetics?'

'Hmmm, that's an interesting idea, but what about the argument that the only way dietetic practice will be affected will be for the dietitians to read about it in one of their own journals?'

'Yes, that is the argument, but it's based on an arrogant assumption that every dietitian receives her or his knowledge from that journal. I would wonder how much of dietetic practice is revolutionized by reading an article in the *Canadian Journal of Dietetic Practice and Research*. It is just such a narrow view of what counts as dietetic knowledge. What you need to do is to publish outside of dietetics and create a critical literature that is taken up by others. We're not the only dietitians who read outside their professional circles. Eventually, the profession will be moved to acknowledge its shortcomings.' Ariana was passionate in her argument for broadening the scope of dietetic practice. 'It just bothers me deeply – the extreme arrogance of it. Not to mention the gate keeping of the peer review process itself. Those with power prevent different ideas from being heard because those readings subvert the dominant ideology, and detractors are kept silent because the powerful won't take the risks, which reinforces the dominant views by default. It is quite sophisticated, really.' Ariana paused, took another sip of tea, and offered in a softer voice, 'Have you considered writing poetry in response?'

Jacqui instinctively thought back to her graduate courses with Dr Rishma Dunlop and her discovery of poetry as a means for articulating her most personal thoughts and feelings. Jacqui received inspiration from Laurel Richardson's insistence that *poetry commends itself to multiple and open readings in ways conventional sociological prose does not* (Richardson, 1992, p. 126). And Heiddeger. *In the age of the world's night, the abyss of the world must be experienced and endured* (Hieddeger, 1971, p. 92). Rishma's own words echoed an urging, a beckoning to shift into the abyss between language and silence, science and art. Jacqui looked over and read the quote that was taped to the edge of her computer monitor, always there, a steady reminder:

> *All art begins in the locations where certainty ends. Poetry begins here, deeply rooted in the ambiguities, blood remem-berings, human obsessions and desires that cannot embody ethics, but may be capable of measures of truth … The place in which a poem begins, this is a dark margin, ambiguous, born of the imagination* (Dunlop, 2002).

Ariana herself was a gifted poet who often shared her love of words with Jacqui. Jacqui turned her attention away from the computer and back to Ariana to reply, 'Hmmm, maybe. I have to admit that the option of publishing elsewhere kinda feels like giving in, but I also have to admit that my creative energies are being strangled in the process of creating an article for dietitians that meets with the approval of not only my so-called peers in nutrition, but also the journal editors. Maybe I just need to be better at the political game, more clever.'

'Yeah, maybe there's some truth to that, but that's also called blaming the proverbial victim. You and I both recognize the structures at play here. The discipline doesn't have a dietetics knowledge preserved for decades at a time without devising some protective measures. If there is one thing you can do it's explore alternate publications and contribute to a larger dialogue, which in reality is going to be read by more people. Then those who have an awareness of a dietetics in disarray will begin to question the profession, urging dietetics to reinscribe themselves. Because right now, others in the "allied health care fields"' – she used her fingers to mark quotes in the air – 'look with disdain on dietetics as fragmented and insignificant. Why do you think our dieti-tian colleagues are so intent on professional recognition? Because they don't get it from their peers and they were promised that they would by those recruiting them into dietetics. Even Dietetians of Canada markets us as "an essential part of a balanced eating plan," right? Remember that poster we just had mailed to us? What did it say?'

'Right, yeah, oh, I have a copy of that here somewhere.' Jacqui reached across to one of her stacks of paper and pulled out a page that unfolded to poster size. 'Yeah, OK, "You can trust Registered Dietitians to give you good advice on nutrition. Their university training has given them the technical knowledge needed to master this most complex science." What do you think of that?'

Ariana's response was incisive. 'That's just incredibly essentialist, medicalizing discourse. And it also positions non-dietitians as incompetent and Other, alien to those in the know. Are dietitians trying to increase troubled eating to ensure jobs? Technical knowledge? How insecure is this? Is empathy technical? Technically, what are they implying about the usefulness of knowledge that is acquired elsewhere? Can non-dietitians contribute to nutrition? What happened to an empowering approach? Patient autonomy?' Ariana was riled. '"Master!" Right. Let's make sure the poster is "manned" while we're at it … images of conquering, disciplining, bringing down to size, dissecting mystery, elitism. I find it completely insulting, so narrow. My point is, when we shift the gaze, the dietetic profession comes under the scrutiny of various knowledges and perspectives, and it cannot escape that gaze, it cannot ignore it any longer … And, I'm quite serious about the poetry, too.' Ariana took a long sip of tea, both hands curled around the cup. She hadn't intended to get so worked up about the poster and Jacqui's experiences, but she also felt a fire raging within. Her desire for dietitians to become more sensitive to the trauma, disability, and discrimination faced by others put her in a position similar to that of Jacqui. Both women felt dismissed and silenced by the profession. Ariana often described the feeling of being misunderstood, of receiving blank stares from her colleagues when she said things like 'the personal is political.' Ariana and Jacqui shared the experience of exclusion from their profession and through reciprocal performatives in their writing and speaking they were sustained – they needed each other, they understood each other. They knew they were not alone.

ða

Jacqui got to school early, intent on accomplishing as much as possible. She opened her email and was pleased to discover a poem from Ariana. Jacqui had taken up Ariana's invitation to issue a poetic utterance, and the creative process had lifted the dark, lingering distress. Both poems were there now, on Jacqui's computer screen, poetic sisters, subject to each other. As usual, Jacqui was drawn up by Ariana's creativity, *when the right word can leave you breathless,* as Rishma said. Ariana's poetry was all this and more – an evocative incantation.

> *Strain*
>
> *I took my tree*
> *and I shook out its roots*
> *and even-emeried its bark in places*
>
> *then when it resembled a symbol*
> *I put this potted garland centre stage, full glare*
> *before the penned-up gardeners*
>
> *and something dropped*
>
> *ah! I had not glossed over threadveins*
> *or cropped the thriving shadows or lop*
> *   -ped the straggling*
> *tips   ruthlessly I did not*
> *   prune the unsmooth*
> *but imagine - I polished the knots to a feature*
> *and let the haggling ivy reflect on from its frightening*
> *triangles*

I made everything mentionable

and mercilessly

something dropped

a kernel,
its scratchy tenacity thirsty for a hungrier shore
and I walked away
impressing the firm dirt with my purpose
into the brusque grain of aloneliness

thinking
densely
of the way the plentiful roots writhe with aliveness

and treasuring also the rustle of the one leaf
that stirred
searchingly

ॐ

Wonderinging

something about autumn
the peculiar dead of things
the heaviness of it all
the wonder worn by rhythms
ringing of trees
takes us to a jutting edge
and there we stand
abreast of nature

then we hear her whispers
'it's who we are'
right there at our side, wondering
'what brought us here?'
lips wrap smiles, hearts spark

'it's who we are'

these differences
our queerness opaque
histories blank as stares
empty canvases
sheets of unblinking whiteness
gaze upon each other
speaking voluminous silences
guessing at desire
just fragments of our longing

languages of water
well known to us
seep through bones of our being
etch the salt of our breath
we taste the bitterness
the peculiar dead of things
it's who we are

no sense to know
know the words
words to songs
songs of science melodic
stings of betrayal injurious speech
words as blades marking what counts
marking our flesh
twisting our tongues
toning us down   down   down

into the roots of that autumn
alive with courage, irreverent
roots gritted black
loving that dirt
loving wildly that dirt
with all her heart

all while wondering why…
the peculiar dead of things

Having received Ariana's gift, Jacqui was feeling open to return to her own writing. The workshop transcripts were compelling. Jacqui had asked participants to bring artefacts of their dietetic education to share with the group; objects that symbolized their memories of some aspect of their educational experience.

During the first workshop, Renny had shared with the group a quilted jacket she had been working on but had never finished. She quit working on it when her father became gravely ill, just before he died. She had just returned to working on the project but wanted to share with the group a part she had sewn years ago. Renny described it as an orthogonal design. She spoke of herself as a very linear thinker and her design reflected that quality; there was no integration. Every aspect of herself was separate. She then spoke of her Portuguese heritage saying, 'I had a very clear sense in my mind that I was Canadian, but I have never felt Canadian even though I was born in this country. This was a purposeful attempt to acknowledge that, yes, I am Canadian, and I have value and I deserve to be here.' She then shared how at the time she was working on defining herself, she was also struggling with an anxiety disorder and how proud she was to talk about it in the group because she hadn't discussed it for so many years. When she turned the jacket over, she revealed a beautiful flourishing tree, which she described as her attempt to honour her roots. Corine remarked, 'It's unfinished because it's your life.'

After a moment of silence, Angela remarked to Renny, 'I totally teared up when you were saying that. I find it incredibly moving when people just go to those depths and share part of who they are with others. I find that very powerful. I thank you.'

Renny responded, 'You're welcome. And, you know, I had an experience of depression and my anxiety and all that was mixed in and I felt really uncomfortable talking to people because nobody knew I was depressed. I just disappeared from work one day and I was gone for six months. I played it really well. I didn't even know I was in trouble. I was very high functioning, there were no overt signs, it was all internalized. One thing that came out my conversation with Jacqui about my anxiety and telling my colleagues about my anxiety was Jacqui's response. She said, "What a gift!" I realized after Jacqui and I talked that by sharing my experience with others, I've given them permission to talk about it and by not doing so I saw myself as part of the problem. So, now I tell people. It has really liberated me in many ways.'

Jacqui was astounded that a colleague could just disappear for six months without warning. In listening to the tapes of that session over and over, she began to understand how they indeed *lived in skittering times and how the old reliables of their invention were beginning to crack.* Jacqui could hear Renny's echo, 'My well was so dry it was starting to crack. I had to leave for my own survival.' Jacqui wondered how many of her colleagues struggled through periods of disintegration, silence, and depression as their reliables skittered and cracked. Their only option to vanish and disappear. What was to become of them?

Chapter Five – Fertile Again

*Our essays are borne up and sung in throats
and written in blood and etched
on skin, then fading, falling,
making soils rich and fertile again.*

(Jardine, 1998, p. 136)

Week 5: October 5

'OK, before we launch into Liquori – hmmm, launching into Liquori, that's quite an image – I would like to create some time for your responses to "Somewhere a dietitian is not complicit." Are there any brave souls who took up my invitation?'

Dani observed Tess to be all business this morning. No introductory remarks, no ramblings. She appreciated the absence of small talk. That kind of conversation just made her impatient. Out of the corner of her eye, Dani saw Meg put up her hand. Dani felt a throb of irritation at the back of her skull. Meg was becoming a little too overbearing in this class, and it was beginning to really grind Dani's last nerve.

'OK. I have something, but I'm not a poet.'

'It's OK, Meg. We are not here to judge your artistry. Please go ahead. No disclaimers.'

'Alright. Yeah, last week I was talking to a dietitian who works in our community. She had immigrated recently to Canada, and she was telling me about the process to become a dietitian in Canada. It really, well, it's pretty incredible. She was a trained dietitian, supervising other dietitians in a hospital in Iran and all that, and then when she got here she actually had to go back to school to prove to the College that she was competent. Anyway, I wrote this about her experience and – well, anyway, here it is.'

Somewhere a dietitian is not complicit …

you took me by surprise
coming to dietetics accidentally
your father wanting a doctor
you desired different
together apart
I am undone by your story

you share my surprise
coming to find an altered experience
of what we call Canadian
criteria shifted under you

ungrounded, but undeterred

you speak to me of your process
inside I flinch
deeply saddened
weary

a mirror appears before me
I am silent, in a far off place
I am complicit
you persist
through the black and blue of it

unjustified
unmarked
untenable
unappreciated

your story unwritten
a diplomat you claim
'I aim to politicize'
such a noble response
I fall short, inadequate

still your light shines and shines
your singing laughter rings
through the narrow cobbled streets
joyful free
finding yourself here despite
shining your light
determined to
be you.'

The room fell silent, everyone taking in Meg's poetic narrative. Finally Tess spoke, 'Yes, Meg, you are a poet.'

Meg looked down then around at the others in the room, a little wary of their responses. They were unequipped for a reply. Meg interpreted the silence a thousand ways.

'Meg, can you say a little bit more about your response to finding out about the process to become what we call a "Canadian dietitian"? I'm guessing from your poem, you didn't realize what was involved?'

'Uh, no. I really had no idea that there was so much involved. I could see that she was passionate about her work and that she tried to put the experience in a positive light. Apparently, she met some really amazing people who helped her through the process, and, even though she said it was incredibly hard, she had no regrets or resentment. I couldn't believe it. I would never have been able to get through all that. I don't know what I would have done. The worst part is that the steps were not really described to her very well before she came, and so, each time she finished something, she had to go through something else that she wasn't expecting. It cost a lot of money. A lot. It makes me feel kinda sad to know that's what the profession will force people to do. I don't know.'

'Does anyone else know about the process that Meg is talking about?'

Several students shook their heads. It made sense to Tess that they wouldn't be aware of the immigration process, given they were so focused on struggling to keep up with academic expectations, volunteer activities, and a variety of part-time jobs. Their worlds were full, too full to take on another's struggle, especially struggles that originated outside their nation's borders.

'I think it might be a good idea to expand on this a bit here. If I miss anything, Meg, just fill in the gaps. OK, so from what I know of it, if you are trained as a dietitian in another country and wish to come to Canada, the federal government is quite encouraging. They tell you that jobs are available in your field and that you just need to have some money to carry you through the transition time. Before you come, you check your credentials with the International Credential Evaluation Services, if I remember correctly, to see if your degree is equivalent to that conferred to a Canadian graduate. The next step is to have Dietitians of Canada assess your qualifications, after which they make recommendations for academic updating or the like.'

Meg interrupted Tess. 'Yeah, Yasma had her degree assessed as equivalent to a Canadian degree, but then Dietitians of Canada made her take four courses when she moved to Canada. She was supposed to go through the provincial regulating body, but they didn't have any guidance for her. I don't know. Even though she had a degree, an internship based on the American system, and had been practising for three years as, … uh, what did she call it, uh … something like sole charge dietitian, with twenty-five people under her, you know, she had to take community nutrition, food quality production, and biochemistry all over again. Like, the university where she wanted to take her courses wouldn't even let her into one course. They said they didn't want to give her someone else's spot and they couldn't deal with one more student. They wouldn't make an exception. Can you believe that? In a foods course? Whatever. So she had to take it by distance ed and pay American dollars, double what she would've paid at a Canadian university. I just don't get it. I don't get it. She says it's a problem with the government, not the provincial dietetics College. The government gave her the impression it would be a lot easier than it was. Yasma said Canadian dietetics did their best trying to turn her away, but she was very persistent. I don't know that I would've been able to do what she did.'

'Well, I think that's the point, Meg. I realize that all of you had to work very hard to get into this program and you should be commended for your efforts. What we're talking about here is something a little different.' Tess didn't want the students to feel guilty. She knew that guilt often precludes action and growth, and probably learning, too. She simply wanted to raise their consciousness about structures that affect their international colleagues' entrance into Canada and the practice of dietetics, processes that affect them all by determining how diverse the profession becomes and how different knowledges are valued. She knew that there were not many practising dietitians trained outside of Canada, but she hoped that would change with time. Tess even heard about a recent research application by the School of Nutrition at Ryerson University in Toronto to examine the process of what they called 'the Canadian experience' for international dietitians wishing to move to Canada. For a short time, there had been a program to provide assistance to internationally trained dietitians at a local college, but she had since heard this program was discontinued, and she did not know why.

Meg's comments reminded her of a book that Ariana had lent her when they met for their inaugural supervision group a few weeks ago. Tess decided to mention it to the class. 'Coincidently, I'm reading a book that relates to this topic. It's called *A Knowing Organization*. I actually have it here.' Tess reached into her large sisal bag, a gift from a friend who recently visited Kenya. She flipped the paperback book open and thumbed through the pages to find what she was looking for. 'OK, where is it, yes: "A knowing organization engages in continuous learning and unlearning of assumptions, norms, and mindsets that are no longer valid, plus mobilizes the knowledge and expertise of its members to induce innovation and creativity" (Choo, 1998, p. 4-5). Given the process our professional organization has deemed necessary to sanction immigrant dietitians, would you say that that organization is a knowing organization? Well, that's what I would call a rhetorical question. Maybe a better question is: What process would a knowing organization offer in the welcoming of dietitians from other parts of the world to work in Canada?'

Dani decided to share her views since she couldn't be bothered to write a response to "Somewhere a dietitian is not complicit." 'It is important not to allow dietitians with substandard knowledge to practise in Canada, so the organization needs to guard against this.'

Tess noticed Dani's use of the word 'guard' as she offered another question to the class. 'What do you imagine it feels like for the woman that Meg describes to us in her poem? How do you think this process has affected her?'

'She probably feels pretty happy now that she's here and all.' Dani stood firm.

'Yeah, it sounds like the poet is more troubled by the experience than this Yasma person.' Candice offered to fuel the debate. She added, 'Why didn't she stay in France?'

'She didn't come from France, actually.' Meg was aware that Candice had not paid attention to her earlier remark about Yasma being from Iran. Meg felt unheard as was becoming familiar among her peers. Meg's voice trailed off as she looked down at her poem and remembered briefly what it was like to write it over the weekend, returning to it over and over again as she attempted to learn the biochemistry of lipid metabolism. The poem tempted her like a plate of freshly baked cookies. She became more than a little obsessed by it, seduced by it, and moved by Yasma's telling of her experience coming to Canada. Yasma's story distracted her, rooted in her pulse. Meg hadn't until then given the process of immigration much consideration. Her mentor at the Downtown Eastside Health Unit had suggested Meg interview Yasma for her course assignment. Over coffee with Yasma, something shifted for Meg, and the coincident invitation from Tess to write about complicity offered Meg a reprieve, a poetic reprieve. To sit in class and hear her peers take up such topics as organizational racism in glib, cavalier ways, misunderstanding her, unsettled Meg even more, but she didn't have the language to respond. She was still in the moment of becoming a poet.

Tess was distracted by the conversation. She hadn't intended to spend so much time on poems. She hadn't really expected the students to respond to her invitation, and Meg's bringing up the topic of immigration and professionalism, was derailing her intention to talk about Toni Liquori's paper. Then she realized that the paper and the poem were related. Her mind spun to make real the segue.

'OK. This may seem a little abrupt, but I was just thinking about Liquori's paper and the way in which she describes the social organization of nutrition professionals. I would like to see if we can connect this topic of a "knowing organization," immigration, and the social organization of nutrition professionals.'

The students visibly groaned and shifted in their chairs, desperate to leave, desperate for the class to be over. Tess's question asked their minds and imaginations to bend in ways they were unprepared and unwilling to accommodate. Tess felt the resistance, but she ignored it temporarily as she turned to write the three concepts on the board then circled them with a flourish.

'OK, who wants to take a try at this?'

No response.

'Alright, OK. Please take out a piece of paper and draw three circles on it like I have drawn on the board. Label each of the circles. OK, now let's try to find the connections and contradictions here that have been raised by the poem, the article, and the quote from *The Knowing Organization*. I'll give you some time right now to speculate on this, so find a couple people to talk to and let's see what we come up with. I'll write the quote from the book up on the board for you.'

As Tess turned to write the quote on the board, students milled around and dutifully reformed in small groups. Amid the noise of moving chairs they began to talk. 'I don't get it.' 'What's the point?' 'Will this be on the midterm, do you think?' 'Are you go-ing to the Odyssey tomorrow night?' Some even began drawing on their pages. When Tess turned back to the students, she took all of it in, breathed deeply, and decided to sit down with one of the smaller, quieter groups, as a pedagogue participant.

'Hi.' Tess felt a little awkward sitting with the students. She sensed their unease with having her there. The discomfort quick-ly disappeared with the first comment from one of the students.

'Well, I'm a little more, but not much … I understand this article, I think.' Marci, who wore simple wire-rimmed glasses, her straight dark bangs falling over her eyes, initiated the con-versation.

Tess smiled at the student's earnestness. 'I would love to hear what you think this article is about and then we can go from there.'

Marci continued. 'Uh, yeah. Jump in anytime guys, help me out here. OK, I get that the author compares two types of knowl-edge, you know, like, scientific and experiential. And I get that the scientific stuff is done by men and the experiential is done by women and the scientific is valued more because it is objective. I get that much.'

'And how would you classify the types of courses you have taken in your dietetics degree?' Tess was impressed and wanted to know more.

Another student responded, 'Oh, that's easy. The science cours-es for sure. Although NUTR 430 has thrown a twist in that for sure.'

Everyone in the group laughed at this remark and the truth of it, how the clean sweep of scientific, abstract knowledge offered in the majority of dietetics courses had been disrupted by discourse analysis, economics, and the sociology of gender and work.

'Don't forget to include our community nutrition course. It seems to look more at the bigger picture, too.' Candice sat with her arms and legs crossed, still sceptical.

Marci was undaunted. 'Yeah, I guess. Anyway. That knowing

organization quote … I'm thinking about the connection between the quote and the article. So, the part about unlearning of assumptions that are no longer valid … I don't see that happening in the organization paper, uh, the Liquori paper. She draws it like there is no connection or overlap between the curves Liquori has drawn in her diagram, you know, no innovation or creativity between the scientists and the women sharing nutrition information. So I see those two as not really connected.'

Tess followed along intently, 'Oh, you mean you don't see a connection between what is described as a "knowing organization" and the social organization of nutrition professionals. I get it. Yes.'

'I kinda get from the description of the Canadian experience process that it's sort of negative. Like, you can't work here if you didn't go to school here. We don't believe you can do it right. You can't do it as good as us. Anyway, like if the system in France – OK, I know she didn't work in France – but if the education system in France is based on the education system in America, what's the big deal? Isn't the Canadian system basically the same as the American system?'

Sammi, a typically quiet student, offered an insightful observation. 'Uh, it's still about what counts, but really it's also about who counts because of the knowledge that they possess or not. Get my point?'

Tess wondered briefly how the other groups were doing, noticing that she was distracted by her shifting attention to the conversations coming from other parts of the room. She couldn't really decipher anything coherent, so she just trusted that it was what it was. She would get a better sense when they reconvened. She wanted to pay attention to what was happening in her own group.

'Yeah, my assumption is that someone trained in, I don't know – wherever … Thailand – needs a certain amount of retraining. So, how do I determine that's wrong?' Marci was testing out her understanding.

'How did you come to believe that to be true in the first place?' Tess quickly interjected, forgetting her intention to be more of an observer, not trying to impose her beliefs, keenly aware of her power to obstruct. She leaned back, hoping to give the other students in her group the sign that she didn't want to take over. Signs could be misinterpreted, however. Tess's question was met with silence.

'Be patient,' a small voice said in Tess's head. 'Just be patient.' Tess breathed. The breathing helped Tess to clear the psychic space to consider other possible explanations.

Marci added, 'I mean, where do these beliefs really come from? That's a hard question. I don't even know if I could answer it.'

Sammi added, 'Yeah, these beliefs are just so ingrained. So, when we stop learning, the assumptions get more, they get stronger, maybe.'

'Hmm … that's pretty insightful. I guess that's where my passion for education comes from – to keep learning, to continually check and recheck my assumptions. Are they still valid?' Tess ignored her own directions to say less.

'Would you call the Canadian experience a racist process?' Sammi was quickly becoming a force in the group.

Although Sammi was staring right at Tess, Tess instead looked to the other students in an effort to deflect the question more towards them. Tess wanted to hear from the others.

'In some ways, yeah, you could say it's racist. But don't forget, dietetics is not the only profession to do it this way. A friend of my dad's came to Canada from India. He was a high-powered engineer in India and now he is a custodian at a law office downtown. It's pretty bad.' Marci responded.

Tess became aware of the time they had spent in their small groups. She assessed that they were not going to resolve the issue of structural racism in this discussion, so she decided to bring the class back together so they might share their comments about the connections and disconnections between the three processes. She was inspired by the students' willingness to delve into areas they were not prepared to go earlier. Her assumptions about them as resistant to learning and dialogue clearly needed to be reassessed.

'Yeah, it is pretty bad, and I hear those comparisons made so often, that it's not just dietetics, but I believe that we can only do so much and since we are here, sharing dietetics as one common interest, we might as well examine its practices as closely and attentively as possible.' Tess paused, to let her statement linger, then added, 'This was good. I appreciate the way you took it to a really meaningful place. Let's get the group together and find out how others interpreted things.'

Tess smiled and stood to ask everyone to come back to the large group. She checked her watch – ten minutes left – and felt that familiar urgency. Too much to hear, too much to say, too little time.

⁓

Gabrielle, Tess, Ariana, and Jacqui were assembled again in Jacqui's office. This time they were joined by Carly, who had agreed to work with them, to facilitate their supervision group. Jacqui was eager to begin, to jump right in, but she was aware that it was the first time for the others and wanted the process to unfold in a way that was respectful. It had taken such a long time to begin supervision with her sister dietitians, that Jacqui didn't want to jeopardize anything. After weeks of planning and ongoing conversations with Gabrielle, Tess, and Ariana, Jacqui had finally convinced them to move forward and hire Carly as their facilitator. Now, it was time for Jacqui to relinquish the role of instigator and simply participate along with the others. She was excited to see what Carly had planned for them.

'Shall we get started?' Carly was a soothing presence in the room. Her tailored grey pants and crisply pressed white shirt exuded an air of competence. She wore no jewellery except a large but simply designed silver ring. The bold ring drew attention to Carly's long fingers and perfectly manicured nails. Her elegant

hands moved gracefully as she spoke. Jacqui caught herself staring and quickly looked down at her own hands, dry and chapped
from washing them so frequently. She felt a twinge of envy. Carly
continued speaking. 'I want to give you an opportunity to share
your feelings about this new adventure as a starting point for
our process. And, instead of the typical intro of who you are and
where you work and how long you've worked there, I'd like to
hear your name and your expectations for this group. And one
other thing, to help me get to know you better could you also
share one word that you feel describes each woman, including
yourself. Who would like to go first?'

'OK, I'll start. I'm Tess. My expectations are pretty minimal
really. I'm open to what might happen, especially being able to
get some support and guidance with my teaching and my nutrition practice. That's about all. I've never done this type of group
before, so I don't have too many expectations about it really. And,
uh, OK, one word ...' Tess paused, smiled. 'OK. Gabi, mischievous, Ariana, sensitive, and Jacqui, determined. There.'

Carly just smiled, her long legs crossed, her body relaxed in the
comfortable office chair.

'Uh, I'll go next. My hope for this group is to share some of the
conflict that I've been experiencing in my work lately and find a
way to reconcile that conflict, inner conflict. Oh, yeah, I'm Jacqui. So, Tess, I would say ... committed, Ariana, poetic, and Gabi
... Gabi is principled. That's it.'

'My turn. I'm Ariana. Hi. I'm here because Jacqui invited me.'
The women laughed, as it really was because of Jacqui's initial
encouragement that they all considered coming together in this
way. 'She may have invited me, but I really do think it is a good
idea and I think for me, it is important to explore how support
from all of you will help sustain me in my work. I'm also struggling with some pretty big dilemmas at work, and I'm this close
to leaving dietetics and writing poetry instead.' Ariana held up
her fingers to indicate just how close she was to making good
on her promise. 'I think that, instead of doing something com-

pletely impetuous, maybe being here with you, my like-minded colleagues, will keep me grounded and connected. It's dreadfully hard working with people who just don't get it, and with all the cutbacks lately, the morale is really low. It's pretty bad, and they want to put in all these standardized practices, and I'm feeling totally against it all, and I'm thinking I must be off, the only one who is sceptical of it all. OK, now I'm babbling.' She looked at Carly and said with an elfin grin, 'So, now you're getting a good sense of me, my daft psyche, my wounded self. I think that's probably enough for now. I don't want you to run straight from the room before we even get started!'

From Carly's posture, there was no indication she wanted to run from the room. Instead, she continued to look intently at Ariana and remarked, placidly, 'Thank you, Ariana. And how would you describe the others?'

'Oh, my God! I'm such a ditz. Can't even follow simple instructions.' Ariana's response suddenly seemed to Jacqui awkward and exaggerated, qualities she did not typically associate with Ariana. Jacqui wondered if Carly had put some kind of spell on Ariana. She began to watch Ariana more closely for signs of something. She briefly wondered if this were what they called 'transference.' Ariana continued, 'Right, Jacqui is highly intelligent, intimidating at times, and prone to secrecy, which can be terribly frustrating for those closest to her.'

'Easy, Ariana. I think she only asked for one word.'

'Then I will change it to annoyingly modest. For Tess, my dear Tess. Only one word comes to mind for you and that is stubborn.' Tess's eyebrows raised. Ariana had hit her mark. 'And, Gabrielle, the luscious Gabrielle ... inspiring.'

Jacqui felt certain by this point that she was seeing a different Ariana. Maybe she should offer her observations to the group as a way of addressing interpersonal dynamics that were sure to arise anyway. Maybe that would be too entirely terrifying and exposing. Instead she crossed her legs and waited for Gabrielle's introduction.

'Wow, thank you for that Ariana. I'm blushing. Wow! Well, like in many things in my life, I kinda just feel like I'm along for the ride, for the adventure, and don't really have any expectations at all of what's to come. I love these women dearly, and my life would be terrible, desolate without them, so when the chance came to be here, to spend more time with my three amazing friends, I obviously couldn't refuse. So, I don't have any expectations, which means I won't have any disappointments either, right? Yeah, right! OK, let me say to you Tess, my mentor-mother, you are the most honest, direct, and dedicated communicator I know and I'm so thankful you are in my life. Oh, God, I'm going to cry now!' The women laughed, and Tess reached for a tissue to offer Gabi. 'Jacqui, where do I begin? Jacqui is a rare blend of compassion and politics, never wavering from her sense of truth and justice.' Jacqui was deeply touched by Gabi's words. Their eyes connected and Jacqui's began to fill with tears. 'Ariana, you are a force, a force! Unstoppable, unafraid, unfettered. That is Ariana.'

Gabrielle, in her characteristic generosity, deftly thwarted Carly's instructions of only one word, taking the opportunity instead to illustrate the essence of each of the women, straight from her heart. This was the spirit that had brought them together and cemented their unique relationship with each other – a group of friends so rare in dietetics, where most practitioners talk about needing to venture outside the profession to find companions. Dietetics was a profession whose foundation was laid with the bricks of competition and individuality, and quite often these attributes survived long after the granting of a university degree. The qualities of autonomy and competition tended to divide, but in the case of these four women, only remnants of that professional foundation remained, and they were intent on fostering their relationships, not dismantling them.

⁂

October 9

Dear Judith,[1]

I was recently speaking with a professor in our faculty about my research. 'Whose theoretical framework are you using to explain your findings?' she asked. 'Uh, Dorothy Smith and Marjorie DeVault,' I stammered in reply. 'Hmmm,' she mused. I sensed my response was not quite enough. 'Given what you know of my work, who would you suggest?' I asked. 'Well, their work is just fine, fine work, indeed, but I'm surprised because they are relatively conservative theorists.' My heart pounded. I waited. 'Have you considered any of Judith Butler's work on performativity?' Well yes I have, but haven't returned to it lately. I admit to being more than a little intimidated by her work. It hasn't come up in any of my classes, so I haven't been able to explore it to the depth I believe it demands.' My speech spilled out of me like bubbles. 'Yes, I understand. I would encourage you to revisit it when you're ready. There's definitely something there for you. Something there that might explain what you're finding with dietitians.' She sat back in her chair. Is that where the hidden theoretical treasures would be found? Judith Butler?

So I write to you now seeking to learn what you have to offer this research. I admit to a superficial grasp of your work. I was drawn to your gendered theories of performativity last year when I was writing my comprehensive exams. Something enticed me even then. I wrote:

> Butler would contest 'that to be *constituted* by discourse is to be *determined* by discourse, where determination forecloses the possibility of agency' (Butler, 1999c, p. 18). One might argue that dietetic socialization enables a dietitian performativity, where performativity is the stylized repetition of acts, continual citing of past practices, and reiteration of known customs. The appearance of 'dietitian' as

---

[1] Letters to Prof Judith Butler have not been posted.

recognizable is 'a performative accomplishment which the mundane social audience, including the [dietitians] themselves, come to believe and to perform in the mode of belief' (Butler, 1999c, p. 179). The dietitian as being/body is 'a variable boundary, a surface whose permeability is politically regulated, a signifying practice within a cultural field of gender hierarchy and compulsory heterosexuality, ... [and] possessing a conditional history with limited possibilities' (Butler, 1999c, p. 177). That the dietitian body, the gendered body, is performative, however, suggests that she has no being apart from the various acts that constitute her dietitian reality. These acts create a deliberate illusion that is discursively maintained for the purposes of the dietitians' own regulation.

So, there you have it, your work ostensibly appropriated for the illumination of dietitian performativity.

When I returned home that day, I told my partner, Kelly, about the decision to read my research results through your theory. 'Be careful,' she warned. 'You better read the critiques before going ahead with it. You have to be able to defend your choice at some point.' Her response may have been somewhat expected, as she took a course in which one of the required texts was your own *Gender Trouble*. The other was Sedgwick's *Epistemology of the Closet* (Sedgwick, 1990). I remember her struggling with your text and debating its usefulness with the hard line of her highlighting pen.

I searched for what your critics were saying of your work. The first piece I read was Love's book review, 'Dwelling in Ambivalence.' 'Ambivalence is the keynote of the philosophical traditions with which Butler has engaged most deeply ... She reminds us that while we continue to try to change the world, we remain deeply tied by desire and the need for recognition to the world as it is' (Love, 2004, p. 18-19). Love's description of your theory not only spoke of my experience but also offered me a way to understand the lives of my research colleagues, my co-inspirators, and myself. Since then I've read more and more and now I write to you in an effort for coherence, in an effort to find meaning.

How ironic, you might think? Coherence? Isn't coherence akin to stability, structure? Can you talk of subjectivity, performativity, and at the same time desire coherence? I'm not entirely sure, but what am I to write if not? What am I to offer? Who am I to try?

In-Coherence,
Jacqui

૨&

'Hi, Tess!'

'Oh, I'm sorry I'm late. A student wanted to talk after class and it seemed important.' Tess effused, breathless.

'It's OK. I brought along some reading. It's nice to get away from the computer from time to time.' Jacqui wished she had brought the novel she was reading, Ann Patchett's *Bel Canto*. Inherently more intriguing than her research texts. Instead, she continued to struggle through Judith Butler's *The Psychic Life of Power*. It was intellectually taxing, but gratifying still.

'Yeah, I bet. I don't spend much time around computers anymore. Now, if I could get out of my car more often, that would be something. It seems like I'm always driving around. Such a pace we're all moving at. Let me get some tea. I'll be right back.'

'Sure.' As Tess walked up to order her tea, Jacqui tried to imagine what her life would be like without her computer. It was impossible! With a little smile, her thoughts turned to wondering how Tess's class was going, what Tess thought of Carly and the group supervision, and how things were at home with Zoë and Michael. Jacqui suspected that there was building tension, with Michael losing his job and Tess having to take on extra consultancy projects. Tess desperately wanted to spend more time with Zoë, but that just didn't seem possible. Those seemed to be the sacrifices of parenthood. If she didn't have the commitment of finishing her dissertation, she would be at the park everyday with Evyn, playing, discovering the world through Evyn's eyes. But instead, she worked to keep up with her deadlines in search of the faculty position that would pull her even further away from her family.

On the way home from school yesterday, sitting on the bus, Jacqui was inspired by 'Poetry in Transit' to write a poem of her own. As she was reading the poem to Evyn, it was all she could do contain her tears – the feeling of love so powerful, so intense, her life made rich and full by that love, parenting an ecstasy she had dreamed not of.

> *Our little girl*
>
> *the blues of her eyes*
> *eclipsing the sun*
> *sheaves of dandelions, daffodils*
> *spilling her arms yellow*
> *her laughter, the grace of great things*
> *our hearts crimson*
> *in the harvest of love for*
> *our little girl*

'Oh, tell me how Evyn's doing? Crawling yet?' Tess guessed correctly at the look in Jacqui's eyes. It was not too hard. Tess had met Evyn early and had instantly fallen under her spell. Who could blame Jacqui for her maternal distractions?

'Oh, she is so great. Making 'ma-ma' sounds and laughing, always laughing. She's so funny, such a great sense of humour. So clever, mischievous. I love her immensely. I never imagined it would be like this.'

Tess smiled knowingly. She, too, never imagined it would be so incredible. It seemed like just yesterday when she held Zoë in her arms after a difficult birth. Oh, the magic of looking down at that sweet bundle, so tiny, dependent. And still, after ten years, Tess couldn't help but be under her spell.

'I know it's amazing. I'm glad you're enjoying it. Not every parent has that experience, that's for sure.'

'Well, there was a terrible bout a few weeks ago when we had to take Evyn to the hospital. She got a virus of some sort, lots of vomiting and diarrhea. We had to take her in because she just wasn't able to keep anything down and she got dehydrated and they had to give her an IV. It was awful, just the most awful thing. So vulnerable on that big bed getting that needle in her hand. And because she's plump, they had problems finding a vein for the IV, so they had to poke her twice, once on each hand. Kelly and I couldn't be in the room for that part. It was excruciating. We could hear her cries from the hallway. We were just standing there, holding each other, crying our eyes out. It was shattering.'

'Oh, poor little thing. It's the hardest thing, a sick child. Is she feeling better now?' Tess was genuinely concerned.

'Yes, it was immediate. She got the intravenous at 1:30 in the morning and then was playing for two hours, keeping us all awake. Awake, exhausted, and relieved.'

'Oh, thank God for that. It happens so fast, the dehydration. I'm glad she's OK. Nothing prepares you for those times. We never had to go through that with Zoë, but there was a whole bunch of other stuff and at times I thought I was going to lose my mind. That's when you need a supportive partner. You need each other, really.'

Jacqui was searching Tess's face for an indication of how things were for her in the supportive partner department. She decided to just ask Tess instead of guessing. 'Speaking of supportive partner, how are things at home with Michael?'

'Uh, OK.' The question seemed to have caught Tess slightly off guard. After a moment, she added, 'Well, it's pretty tough actually. I'm working these two jobs and trying to keep it together and he's just moping around. I think he's depressed, but what can I do? His family is not helping matters. Every time we go to their place for dinner, his mom insists that he just relax and read the paper or watch TV while she and I make dinner. I can't believe it! I've worked all day and he's done nothing and I have to make dinner and clean up. Mind you, it's been like that his whole life.'

The loving traditions between a mother and her first-born son were not likely to accommodate Tess's desire for equality.

'And then he expects to be thanked when he does have dinner for us when I get home late or when he does an errand for me. I have to ask him to please pick up Zoë for her riding lessons after school and he looks at me like I've lost my mind. It's like I'm fighting his cultural norms and the fact that he's unemployed right now. I hope that this is a temporary adventure, because my patience is wearing a little thin.'

Jacqui didn't really know what to say. It was hard to be impartial. She cared for Tess and didn't want to see her struggle with life. She was tempted to make some glib remark about being glad she was not living with a man. Two women raising a child and maintaining a household worked just fine for her. But she knew that kind of remark wouldn't give Tess the support she needed. Instead she asked, 'Is there anything that Kelly and I could do for you – frozen dinners, chores, watching Zoë?'

'Thanks, Jacq. I appreciate your offer, but that's just the point. Michael is fully capable of doing those things. Sometimes I feel like I have four or five jobs – two out of the house and two when I get home. I'm going to have to talk to him. It's getting to that point. And I worry, what kind of message it sends Zoë when she sees her mom working, cooking, cleaning, doing laundry, and everything else while her father sits on the sofa and reads the paper and watches TV. What kind of role modelling will that be for her?'

Jacqui was wondering the same thing. She realized she had her own concerns about gender stereotypes. Ever since she and Kelly had made a mandatory visit to the staff counsellor at the fertility clinic before their insemination, they had become a little more guarded in speaking to people about bringing children into a same-sex relationship. It was like they lost their innocence a little bit that day, their anticipation tainted. The counsellor had trotted out spectacularly antiquated chapter and verse, on how lesbians shouldn't talk disparagingly about men in front of their child and that it would be important to have strong masculine role models, like men who were mechanically inclined, for the child to learn from and admire. The whole experience was surreal and outrageously heterosexist. They had wondered whether a heterosexual couple would have been encouraged to prepare for their assisted pregnancy in the same way. Would Kelly have been as marginalized if she had been a man and Jacqui had been experiencing infertility issues? Coincidentally, Kelly had arranged for a researcher to visit them at their house that very evening to talk about the legal issues for same-sex parents. It was a topic they had become almost expert in, especially Kelly – their parental rights were something they didn't want anyone infringing on, now or in their future.

Jacqui's thoughts returned to Tess's problems. 'Yeah, that's pretty hard. Have you ever tried to talk to him about it?'

'Ages ago, but these are long-standing patterns of behaviour. His mother has taken care of him her whole life, and it continues to this day. And to make it more offensive, it's exactly what his dad expects his mom to do. I feel pretty insignificant in the face of that patriarchy. It's stifling.'

Jacqui agreed. She felt stifled just talking about Tess's situation. It was like a choke hold on her throat and brought back memories of her own marriage and the verbal abuse, manipulation, power imbalance. It really wasn't a matter of culture, entirely. Some men – perhaps most men – were well aware of their privileged role: they were simply not willing to seriously question that privilege. In these cases, women experienced further subjection through their male partner's choices. What would Judith Butler say? Precisely at the moment in which choice is impossible, the subject pursues subordination as the promise of existence. Subjection exploits the desire for existence, where existence is always conferred from elsewhere; it marks a primary vulnerability to the Other to be (Butler, 1997, p. 21). But could Tess or anyone else ever fully step outside of that exploitation? Perhaps she could not.

'You know, instead of burdening you with all of this nonsense, can I ask you about what happened in class today?'

'Of course! Yes!' Jacqui was eager to be part of the experience after working with Tess on the syllabus.

'So, after class, this young woman, who shall remain nameless, approaches me to talk about her meeting with a dietitian who just immigrated to Canada. The student was interviewing her for one of our class assignments, and the dietitian told her a pretty harrowing tale of organizational resistance. Maybe more like structural oppression, really. Anyway, she had written a poem about being complicit, a powerful poem, actually, and she shared it in class, which I thought was brave of her. I've asked that more students bring in their poetry to share, so we'll see how that goes. And so, she's just really down about becoming a dietitian. After class she said to me, "Why would I want to become a member of an organization that promotes such practices?"'

'Hmmm … pretty good question. She sounds pretty astute, this student.' Jacqui was keenly interested in Tess's story. She wondered if the dietitian Tess was talking about was actually one of her research participants. Her story was strikingly familiar and the dietetics community was surprisingly small.

'Yeah, she is very aware, very conscious of her world. I'm enjoying her presence in the classroom immensely, although I'm sure some of the other students are starting to feel less embracing of her contributions. Anyway, I just feel we have to be honest with these students about two things: dietetics is emotional and political. So, that's what I said to her. I really would hate to see her abandon her studies now, but I would understand if she did. What do you think? Did I say the right thing? Do you think I misled her or, worse, scared her?'

'No, not at all, Tess. I think she's lucky to have someone like you as her instructor. What was it that David Orr (Orr, 1994) said, 'Without significant precautions …,' uh, what is the rest? Oh, yeah, 'Without precautions, education can equip people to be more effective vandals of the earth.' He says we need fewer successful people and more peacemakers, healers, restorers, storytellers, and lovers. So true. I think we need more dietitians who are all those things, too. This student sounds like she has the potential to be a poet-storyteller. I think she should be encouraged, but with her eyes wide open. We all need support to get through the tough times, the conflict, the strife. That's why I'm so pleased we are finally starting the supervision group. Hey, maybe you want to start a similar group for students? Why not?' Again Jacqui spoke beyond Tess's question and did so unabashedly.

'Well, let's just see how *our* sessions go first, OK?' Tess smiled at Jacqui. She had many ideas, most of them good, some of them great, but all of them beyond what Tess was capable of enacting at this point in her life. It didn't matter, though. Their relationship was what mattered, and Tess was feeling full of craving a sense of the possible, unburdened by what was happening at home, and desiring more connection. All the good things in terms of growth-fostering relationships (Baker Miller & Pierce Stiver, 1997).

'And, now, time to get back in my car. Are you ready to go?'

'Yes, mostly. I think I'd much rather sit here in this tea house for the next three hours than return to my writing!'

'Hey, I get it. Dream big!' Tess leaned in for a quick hug and then dashed out the door ahead of Jacqui, waving over her shoulder. Jacqui waved back, and just as quickly as Tess left the tea-shop, Jacqui's thoughts returned to her writing and her first research workshop. As part of introductions during each workshop session, participants were invited to select a card, an intention card, on which was printed a single word. Desiree spoke to the word 'harmlessness,' which appeared on the card she chose. She spoke of her grandma's Métis heritage and how she had learned to cherish the First Nations way of life, a way of helping heal pain, of women using all that they knew of survival and adapting that knowledge to help others. Jacqui remembered her talking about how mentorship early in her dietetics career protected her from harming others. Desiree ended her introductory remarks with her wish that Jacqui's research would help protect the new ones from the harmful aspects of dietetics. Jacqui found herself preoccupied by Desiree's comments. What were the harmful aspects of dietetics? Jacqui wondered if her research had the capacity to fulfill Desiree's wish. Following Desiree's lead, Valerie hoped the research would emphasize that the tools needed to do their jobs were so much more broad than what was provided by their education. Renny expanded the tool metaphor: 'We all had our hammer stage because that's how we were taught.' Jacqui remembered Renny adding, 'I look back at how I used to work and I cringe.' Renny thought that if undergraduate students were introduced to aspects of spirituality, they would have a greater capacity for dietetic practice and be able to ask patients 'What do you need from me?' instead of hammering people over the head with nutrition facts, especially because patients would sometimes hurt themselves with the knowledge provided by dietitians. Jacqui's thoughts returned to Renny's question about what form the research should take. Renny had asked Jacqui how she was going to disseminate the wisdom the women had to share. At the time, Jacqui didn't have a good answer, but as she pored over these transcripts, hearing the voices and the passion and the melancholia, Jacqui imagined *essays borne up and sung in throats and written in blood and etched on skin* and hoped her representational choices would not disappoint, but instead *make the soils rich and fertile again.*

Chapter Six – Gentle Conspiracy

*Passion disturbs conventional notions of intimacy,
offers new possibilities and new beginnings, brings fresh and not
necessarily pleasurable attitudes, feelings,
and inclinations to self and others.*

(Billow, 2003, p. 218)

Week 6: October 12

'Good morning! Hello!' Tess attempted to gather the students' attention. It seemed they were more energized than ever this morning. As much as it pleased Tess to see them interacting with such abandon, she was reminded of the structures that kept her on track. Because she was already one full class behind and having to decide what to cleave off the syllabus, Tess was moved to begin, and to begin with a surprise.

'OK, this energy is wonderful and will be even more useful if you transfer it towards your pop quiz. Yes, you heard me right. I'm going to give you a pop quiz, for marks, on today's reading by DeVault.'

There was an immediate silence and then some groans and one question, 'I thought we were supposed to be reading Buchanan for today.'

'You are right. We were supposed to be talking about Buchanan today, but since I told the story of Amy three weeks ago, we are going to be perpetually one week behind in our syllabus. It's very good you are prepared to discuss Buchanan. You will have less reading to do for next time. This time, however, the quiz will be directly related to DeVault's most interesting chapter, "Whose Science of Food and Health?" Please take out a piece of paper and write your name on the top corner. Are you ready? Five questions, two points each. You will each mark someone else's paper. Your results will make up ten per cent of your participation mark, so three per cent of your final grade.'

Tess suspected that the talk of final grades, per cents, and such contributed to some anxiety for the students, so she added, 'Do your best.'

'OK, first question, multiple choice: Marjorie DeVault is a) a dietitian, b) a biochemist, or c) a sociologist? Dietitian, biochemist, or sociologist?'

The students who read the paper wrote sociologist down on their pages and looked up at Tess in seconds. Most of the other students continued to look down at their blank pages.

'Number two: How would you describe the theoretical framework and method that DeVault uses in her research?'

Tess gave the students some extra time with this question, especially when one student looked up from her page and said, 'Huh?'

'Theoretical framework. What ideological lens does DeVault look through when she explains her findings to us? We talked about ideology when we discussed Travers's paper in week two. And method. What is the philosophical basis for how she reads the findings of her study, how she analyses her data? There is one answer for both theory and method. Take a minute to think about this one.'

After a short pause, Tess said, 'Number three.'

'Wait! Hold on! Just a sec!' A chorus of annoyance erupted from the class.

Tess stopped, took a drink of her coffee, and gave them more time. Part of her felt uncomfortable pulling the pop quiz for today's class, but she had been wondering just what students were taking from the readings before they met. Since only a few participated in class discussions, Tess was curious about what was going on for students during the time between reading the material and coming to class, with the assumption that students actually read the assigned material. What did they understand from the text that she had offered?

'OK, number three, another multiple choice: According to DeVault, scientific knowledge of food and nutrition is organized around a) a food guide, b) an arbitrary set of rules and standards, or c) a paradox? Food guide, rules and standards, or paradox?' Tess paused briefly.

'Number four: Based on DeVault's research with dietitians, give one reason dietitians enter the profession, one reason that these women choose to go into dietetics.'

Again, a little more time than for the previous question. Tess looked down at the page she was reading her questions from. She wanted to try something different with the final question and wasn't sure how it would work. She was going to try it anyway.

'OK, now for a little twist on the usual pop-quiz format. Before doing the last question, I would like everyone to give her quiz to a neighbour and then switch with one more person.' Papers shuffled. 'OK, good. Does anyone have her own quiz? No? OK. Now just put that quiz to the side and take out a fresh sheet of paper. For the final question, I would like you to pull out your copy of DeVault's chapter and scan through it and write down the one question that you still have after reading the article. What is the one question that remains for you? Maybe it's one of the questions from this quiz, which would be fine, or maybe its something else. You decide.'

Tess could see that many of the students were reading the article and writing intently. It seemed that this may be the easiest question to answer of them all.

'OK, now make sure your name is written on top of that page, too and exchange it with someone else. OK, wait … here, can you two switch again? OK, good. I think we have it. Let's start by marking questions one to four.'

Papers shuffled while pens and minds were primed to normalize knowledge.

'Now, what's the answer for question one?'

Meg responded immediately, 'C.'

'Yes, C. Marjorie DeVault is a sociologist who performs sociological research with dietitians. DeVault is one of the few who does research with dietitians on identity and socialization, actually, which I find somewhat ironic. There aren't many dietitians contributing to the theory of dietitian identity and professionalization. I often wonder why that is the case. Anyway. Good, Meg. Number two. DeVault's theory and method. What's it called?'

Silence this time. Tess waited. A hand went up at the back of the class.

'Is it feminist, uh, feminism?'

'Yes, feminist theory and method. DeVault calls this particular method a 'liberating method,' which is also the title of one of her books. She is a proponent of feminist approaches because they are most concerned with social justice and equity. Are there any other responses?'

'What about "sociological theory and method"?'

'Hmm. "Sociological" is a rather broad rubric. It's more of a discipline than a theory or method. I don't think so. Any other possibilities?'

'This person wrote, "Qualitative."'

'Well, yes, it is a qualitative methodology, but not qualitative theory. So, give only one point out of two. Can anyone find a quote from the text where DeVault talks about feminist theory or method?'

Sammi read from her copy of the article. 'Uh, page 140. "In this chapter, I propose a feminist rationale for renewal of the long-standing sociological concern with professional socialization and work, especially in the so-called women's professions." But, Tess ... uh, look. In the very next sentence she mentions the 'disciplinary "lens" of sociology, so that is kinda confusing.'

Tess suspected that the student was advocating for marks for the 'sociological' response, and she had a point. 'You know, you are quite right. Let me stand corrected on that. Sociology is still a discipline but can confer a particular lens to research method. Let's compromise with giving anyone who wrote "sociological" one point out of two. Fair enough?'

Sammi nodded, and the student marking her paper scratched out the '0' and wrote in a '1'.

'Are we ready to move to question three … anyone?'

Dani responded this time, 'Yeah, the answer is c) paradox.'

'That is correct. Right from the first line in the chapter. Does everyone know what 'paradox' means?'

Tess waited, forming a response in her mind. After a few seconds, she shared, 'A paradox is a statement that seems to contradict itself, even if it is truthful. So, while nutritional science knowledge claims are …, where is it here?' Tess looked to her copy of DeVault's article. 'Yes, "abstract, timeless, replicable, and universal … the activities of producing, distributing, and using food … are more obviously relational, contextualized, politicized, and embodied activities." DeVault and Smith tell us this paradox is "managed, and at least partially obscured by a gendered division of labour" (Smith, 1987, p. 83-84). Some of you might remember Liquori building on the notion of gendered division of labour in her article. Remember the graphics that looked like camels' humps? That was the point she was trying to make with those images. Male nutritional scientists working with abstract knowledge in the food and health care industry – food as marketable products and food as nutrients – while female practitioners work with experiential knowledge of food as nurturance. What is valued most is that which is most scientized, right? The marketable products and the nutrients.'

Tess paused, aware that she was talking at the students. She needed to hear someone's voice. 'OK, let's move on to question number four. According to DeVault's research participants, why do women enter the profession of dietetics?'

'Pays well,' responded Dani.

Marci added, 'They're good at science.'

From Sammi, 'Want to make a difference.'

Dani added with a smile, 'Want a real job after graduating.'

Meg suggested, 'Going to college makes women feel secure.'

Marci stated, 'Want to help people eat healthy.'

'Good, yes, any others that you can think of that weren't mentioned in the article?' Tess hoped students might share their own reasons for entering the field.

Dani remarked, 'Family pressure to enter some health-related profession.'

Meg, in a familiar righteousness said, 'Wanting to learn about nutrition to help people live healthier lives.'

Marci, in a small voice from the back of the room, 'To help people have control.'

And then quiet. The often thought, but rarely spoken, connection between food and body – the disciplining of bodies through the use, actually more the restriction, of food. Tess knew Foucault had something to say about this association, but she decided to leave Marci's comment alone for the time being, to just let it settle there among the other comments.

'Lots of good reasons to come to dietetics, aren't there? Did we get them all?'

No one spoke, so Tess carried on. 'OK, I'm very curious as to which questions still remain about the article. Let's start at the front of the room and if you could read out the question that your colleague shared with you.'

As each student read aloud, Tess felt hopeful that the exercise would work out. 'Excellent! Great! OK, now what I would like each of you to attempt to do is to answer the question that is in front of you. No, it may not be your question, but that's the point. You will get your question back and then you will give the answer a mark out of two, so you will need to know who answers your question. Does that make sense? So, write your name beside the response. Let's leave the rest of the class for you to craft your response, using DeVault's article as your primary reference. When you are finished, please return the page to the person who wrote the original question. And when you're finished reading the response, give the response a mark and then you can return everything to me, so I can record the marks. After you are finished you are free to go. Any questions?'

Tess trusted that her explanation wasn't too confusing. The students gave no indication of confusion and started their responses. Tess finished the remainder of her cold coffee and hoped the pop-quiz activity had a modicum of usefulness for the students. They were now halfway through the term, getting into a routine, and entering the most challenging portion of the course, also known as 'storming' in the group process. Tess imagined means to dissolve problems before they arose. Giving clear instructions was part of that intention. Knowing that her style was more emergent and inquiry-based than didactic and structured, Tess worried that the direction was not always clear for her students. She realized that emergent was not always conducive to predictability. Tess prepared for stormy times ahead.

ళ

Jacqui was back at work after spending the week writing, attempting to complete a first draft of her dissertation. Her first session was with Jane. Jane's therapist, Monica, had been in telephone contact with Jacqui, keeping her updated on Jane's condition. Last week, Jane was admitted to emergency. She had been experiencing fainting spells and heart palpitations. She lasted only one day in the hospital and then was discharged. Both Monica and Jacqui were beginning to get frustrated with the eating disorder program's reluctance to admit Jane. Jacqui had made numerous calls to the program director regarding Jane's deterioration. He insisted they were doing all they could, but the space just wasn't available. In her conversation with one of the program's nurse coordinators to find out what their contingency plan might be, Jacqui listened as she remarked that Jane had many people calling on her behalf and complained that it was becoming difficult to keep everyone informed. Jacqui felt both chastised and defiant. Her intention was to support and advocate for Jane's admission. She knew Jane was at a point of no return, her physical symptoms of starvation precluding any real chance of recovery as an outpatient. Still the structures of the overtaxed medical system were not yielding to human suffering. All Jacqui could do was try to reassure Jane that soon there would be a space available to her and, in the meantime, attempt to provide the kind of support that Jane required – unconditional compassion, encouragement, peacefulness – all of which Jane was not receiving at home.

'Hi, Jane. Come in.' Jacqui greeted Jane at her office door. She was alone today. Rachel must have dropped her off and gone to run an errand. Jacqui was once again shocked by Jane's appearance, although she tried to hide her reaction behind the guise of a calm smile. Jane moved slowly, cautiously, barely able to offer a smile in response. Her eyes were dull, her hair limp, her body fragile. Jacqui found herself moving more deliberately and carefully in response to Jane's obvious body language. Jane took a seat on the couch, gingerly. A shadow of dread passed over the windows as the sun disappeared behind errant clouds. The light faded.

'Have you heard anything from the program in the last couple of days?'

'No, they said they would call me early next week.'

'Oh, well, that's encouraging.'

'Well, I'm not exactly sure what they are going to tell me since they predicted it would be another month or so before a space became available. I'd be willing to take any bed at this point, even if I had to be admitted to the psychiatric unit.' Jane was speaking softly, carefully enunciating each word as it passed her dry lips. There was no cadence to her speech, just the steady, monotonous affect of anorexia.

'Is that an option – I mean could you be admitted to another ward while you wait for a bed?'

'They don't really like doing that because you are with a bunch of other people that, it just isn't good and staff don't really get it. Once, when I was admitted like three years ago, it was the psych unit and this nurse just looked at me when she came to get my tray and said, "I see you didn't eat anything again. You know if you just ate, you wouldn't be in here. Can't you see the hurt you are causing your family?" That was pretty brutal. Like I don't know what's going on. Like it's so easy for me to eat. Trust me, I know the hurt I'm causing and it doesn't help me recover. Why don't people understand that?'

Jane was asking questions whose answers lay deeply tangled in complex familial and social webs, complicated by economic politics, sexism, racism, and homophobia. And that was just the beginning. Once young women internalized messages about how their femininity was valued in silent and subservient ways, it could become very difficult to mount a resistance. Thinness was prized among women. They were, on the one hand, offering their lean emaciated bodies to a male gaze as a form of accomplishment, but, on the other hand, they were killing themselves in the process. Jacqui remembered attending a conference session on recovery from anorexia in which a researcher had given the research participants pseudonyms that were names of plants and trees. This raised a red flag for Jacqui. Seeing women objectified in this way soundly reiterated the problem that existed for women. Even though it might have been thought artful to call the women Ivy, Rose, or Iris, to Jacqui it was an affront of the greatest magnitude. There was one other possibility. Perhaps the researcher was intending to illustrate the overwhelming influence of patriarchy and oppression by naming his participants after plants. Then it would have been sheer genius. And now before her sat Jane, a woman struggling for life amid the stultifying effects of that patriarchy, that insatiable capitalist appetite for materiality. There she sat, so quiet and still, a symbol of the slow, silent death of the feminine. Jane and Jacqui had had those conversations months ago, and still Jane was *deeply tied by desire and the need for recognition to the world as it is.* Jacqui stayed still and quiet until Jane broke the silence.

'Jacqui, how do you feel about death, about dying?'

Silence. Jane looked up and her eyes met Jacqui's. Was that

defiance Jacqui detected, a fire? Jacqui did not look away. She searched for a response.

'Have you been thinking about death lately, Jane?' Jacqui sensed a softening as Jane began to talk.

'Sometimes that's all I can think about. Dying. You know, everyone around me, they pretend that I'm OK, that I'm doing OK. Even up until last week, people were still saying to me, "Oh, you look so good. Wow!" What is wrong with people? Can't they see I'm in so much pain? I mean look at me. I'm disgusting!'

'It's hard to know why people choose to react the way they do. I'm sure they would like to say something more respectful, but maybe their fear of saying the wrong thing just makes it worse for them. What do you think?'

'I think they're totally insensitive and blind. When I get through this and I'm teaching, I will never, *never* say such things to my students if they have an eating disorder. What people need is understanding, not judgment, and not praise for losing weight.' Jane crossed her arms, closing off. Jacqui heard talk of Jane's future, which was reassuring, but still felt compelled ethically to understand Jane's thoughts of death.

'When you think about dying, what exactly do you think about? Can you tell me a little more about that?'

'Well, I just think about how peaceful it would be for me right now. I think, like, it's such hard work to get better. I do want to get better, but it's so hard for me. Why can't I do it? I want to do it, but I just can't. It's too hard. I'm so weak.'

'Jane, I have to ask you this. How far have your thoughts of suicide gone? Have you considered specifically how you might commit suicide?'

'Oh, God, no. I would never actually do it, Jacqui. I could not do it because I love Brandon and I promised him I would be there for him. Although, I'm hardly there for him these days. What a failure I am. Poor Brandon. I've disappointed him, too.'

'Jane, I know it is hard right now, but you are a very brave and resilient woman. You will get better. Remember the symbol you imagined as your strength, the drawing you did with the colours and the healing force? Remember what you told me about that symbol?' Jacqui attempted to speak to hope.

'Yeah, I guess so.'

'You created that symbol. You know you have the strength and the wisdom in you to recover. I believe in you, Jane. You're a fighter and it will be hard, but you have a lot of support. Many people care deeply for you and we all want to see you make it through this. We know you can get through this. You and Brandon can look back on this time and be amazed and inspired by all that you resourced from within to get through this difficult time.' Jacqui sounded like a coach. Her words were really just willing Jane to stay alive. She pulled out all the stops, the tired clichés, anything to rally Jane's spirit. This was Jacqui's response, a response of abiding love.

'Jane, I believe that you are choosing life today, in this moment your choice is a miracle that saves our world. Do you know what I mean by that?'

'Maybe. I don't know. Sure.' Jane paused. Jacqui waited. 'You think that if I can get through this mess, anything's possible!'

'Well … yes! I do believe that and I do believe you will get through this mess as you call it. What I also mean is that by going through this experience, you are learning so much about yourself and the act of knowing yourself is what makes the world a better place. We all have that responsibility, to know who we are, to wonder. Remember what I told you about the "silver lining" of an eating disorder?' Jane nodded. 'Well, by going through this experience, you have grown in profound ways. Do you feel that?'

'Sometimes, yeah.'

'Your growth and knowing of yourself is a gift. Learning to respond to your intuitive voice, your inner wisdom is a gift that you have offered yourself. You will always have that resource available to you, that guiding, knowing, loving inner strength and relational resilience. When things are becoming off-balance in the future, you will have your intuition to tell you ahead of time and you can respond in compassionate ways before it gets too big and dark. You have this gift right now. It will sustain you through the challenges of recovery.'

'I know. I feel that. Yeah. Sometimes the inner voice seems so quiet, though. The critic so angry and dominant. Like, I can't really ignore it. It's so ugly, so mean to me.'

'It's fear, Jane. Try to be gentle with yourself. Imagine a fearful child. How would you respond to her?'

'I'd hug her and tell her it's OK. I'm here to protect her.'

'That's what you need to say to yourself, too. That's a desire for connection alive in you. Shift the inner dialogue whenever you can, Jane. For something so simple, it makes a profound difference.'

'I know. I know. I do my best.'

'You are very resourceful, Jane. I know you will get through this.' Jacqui still had her doubts, though. Her motivational speech was as much for her as for Jane. Jacqui willed the words to become a positive reality.

'What are you noticing right now as we come to the end of our session?'

'Well, I feel pretty good. I'm calm, hopeful, I feel grounded, actually. I haven't felt this way in quite awhile.'

'What can you do to take care of yourself this afternoon? What can you do to nourish yourself while you are in a calm and hopeful state?'

'Uh, I don't know. Maybe I'll go for a walk by the ocean with Rachel after or we'll get a movie. I don't know. I don't really have any plans, really.'

'Is there any possibility of something to eat? Something small even?' Jacqui pushed a little more than usual, just out of desperation more than anything. She sensed Jane was so close to the edge, perilously close.

'Maybe. I probably should. Like what? What do you suggest?'

Jacqui knew if she made a suggestion, Jane would counter it with a brilliant reason why she couldn't. It was a little game of exchange the nutrition info and, although it had its use in a therapeutic context, now was not the time for that particular sport. 'You decide. You know best what it is you need, and you have a great support in Rachel. Ask her to help you, to be there for you while you eat. You have all the resources you need, right there inside you.' Jacqui placed her palm over her heart to indicate to Jane to listen to her intuition, to create a space for herself in her body, to choose life.

As they stood together, Jacqui walked over and embraced Jane, her usual generous and robust hugs restrained for Jane's sake. Jacqui gently placed her arms around Jane and wished only goodness for her. She felt her hands on Jane's back, felt her ribs, her smallness and let all her love flow into that tiny body. After Jane had left, Jacqui felt the full impact of turmoil, fear, and frustration. And yet, there were three more women to see that afternoon. Jacqui took a deep breath and went to the bathroom to boil some water for tea. As she was waiting, she looked into the mirror. She saw lines of worry creasing her brow, she instantly softened her eyes, asking for clarity of vision, compassion, and hope for her remaining time at work. She thought of the Judith Duerk poems, *how might our lives be different,* and she realized that in the doing of this work, she had the privilege to imagine daily how lives might be different, and that this was the hard work that love demanded. This was the hard work she was not prepared for by her schooling, but had learned much later from relational-cultural theorists (Baker Miller & Pierce Stiver, 1997).

ે

October 13

Dear Judith,

I just finished reading Martha Nussbaum's (Nussbaum, 1999) scathing critique of your work and then the replies from Spivak and others, including yours (Butler, 1999b). Quite a process, the whole enterprise of academic debate. And this one, so public, with your response appearing in the *New York Times*. What was it like to have your work taken up in that way? I'm always curious about the personal as subtext to the political, the back story, as they say. Why is the personal so often relegated to the back story?

One of your ideas in the op/ed piece was the notion of complicating common sense as a means for social change, the relation of language and politics – scholars are obliged to question common sense ... if that common sense preserves the status quo and especially if that common sense treats unjust social hierarchies as natural (Butler, 1999a). Yes, I agree. That is not the contentious point. What I've been struggling with is a point you make further along when you address the scholar's pedagogical responsibilities. *A student for whom a word such as 'hegemony' appears strange might find that it denotes a dominance so entrenched that we take it for granted, and even appear to consent to it – a power that's strengthened by its invisibility.* But what of a professional student, a nutrition student, a person who is caught up in the often scientized performative of medicine and health? Does that person have the ability – yes, ability – to discover hegemony as visible in her world, a world she shares with us? And what of her educators, not those with proclivities to the politics of rhetoric, comparative literature, or philosophy, but those possessing prestigious science doctorates, trained in the interpellational act of objectivity and value-neutral truth claims. How might those people take up *the intellectual resources necessary to make our way towards the politically new*?

My quandary is this: If dietetic practice is positioned, and thus reconstituted, by citational apoliticality, and this performative voraciously buttresses hegemonies of the unrepentant variety, should not dietetic students be educated in ways, no, rather, offered discourse that can *help point the way to a more socially just world*? 'Not undergraduates,' they say. They won't understand. 'Not interns.' Too busy learning other things. 'Not practitioners.' No support for that kind of learning. But when? Muriel Rukeyser's *Who will be the throat of these hours?* comes to mind. Is it too radical?

I think the propensity to status quo, those whose very foundations of ordinary life are enmeshed in dietetic education as is, would have me believe that what I'm proposing is indeed radical. The renewed, fervent conservatism.

When I asked one of my research co-participants whether she believed there was an active conspiracy at play, she responded with 'Yes, it is a conspiracy. It's just not active!'

In-active,
Jacqui

સ્

Dani knocked on Alice's door. She had finally summoned the courage to talk to Alice about Tess and her misgivings with NUTR 430. She was nervous about what she was going to say to Alice, but she couldn't stay quiet. Today was one of the few days that Alice was in her office. Dani waited for twenty-five minutes while Alice met with the several students ahead of her in a line that had formed fifteen minutes before Alice's office hours had started. Alice was still the dietetics program advisor, so her opinion on a variety of issues was required. It seemed like a great investment of Dani's time, but she saw no other option.

'Yes, come in.' Alice looked up from her computer as Dani walked in. 'What can I do for you?' Alice asked even before inviting Dani to sit down. Alice was not making it any easier for Dani to say what she needed to say.

'Hi, uh, well I have some concerns about NUTR 430, and I thought I should let you know what's going on in class.'

'What are your concerns?'

'Um, well, like I don't think, I mean I think we're spending too much time on stuff that is totally unrelated to dietetics and the teacher doesn't really seem to know where we're supposed to be going half the time.'

'Have you shared your concerns with Tess directly?' This was the absolute last thing Alice wanted to deal with right now, so she found a way to delay the inevitable.

'No, not exactly. I mean I thought I should let you know what's happening since it is your course and ...'

Alice stopped Dani mid-sentence, 'Yes, I have taught the course for the last couple of years, but this year it is Tess's responsibility, so I would advise you to speak directly to her about your concerns.'

Dani sensed that Alice wasn't going to suggest anything else, but she had waited too long for her time with Alice to be over that quick.

'I'm worried that if I get a poor mark in this class, it will affect my application for internship. I have to do well. I have to.'

'I understand that and I still think you need to talk to Tess first. If things don't go satisfactorily with Tess, then the three of us can meet together. No one else has mentioned any problems with the class, so I would hope that you can work this out with Tess.' Alice regretted offering Dani a meeting with the three of them. She could see this becoming dreadfully time consuming.

'Uh, OK, so I'll talk to Tess, and if she doesn't seem to get it, then I can arrange another meeting with all of us?' Dani paused and considered her options. 'Um, well, I'm a little worried that by the time all that happens, a lot of time will have passed and it will be too late. So, can you at least talk to Tess about my concerns?' Dani thought this would be easier, but Alice wasn't giving her much sympathy. This only made Dani more insistent.

'I don't think it will be necessary for us to meet again. Tess is an excellent teacher and communicator. I'm sure you two will be able to come to some resolution about whatever it is that you're bothered by.' Alice paused and decided on a different tact. 'One thing about being a professional is being able to work with people you might not agree with, Dani. I know Tess has spent much time on this course and although it is different than when I taught it last, I believe it's probably better. Please, go set up a meeting with Tess and just email me afterwards with your thoughts on how it went. OK?' Alice was finished.

'I guess. OK.' Dani stood up to leave, feeling a little more than deflated and dismissed in her exchange with Alice. Alice said nothing as Dani turned and walked out. As she passed the other students waiting to see Alice, Dani thought this was going to be a little trickier than she had anticipated, but she would not be deterred. She didn't get this far to have her goals derailed by a replacement instructor in the second-last semester of her program.

ъ●

Carly entered the counselling room. She smiled warmly and quietly took the last remaining seat among the four other women already present. Since their last meeting only three weeks ago, Carly had found herself thinking about the work that she had entered into with this group of women. Although she had never worked with dietitians before, she found their preoccupations similar to that which psychoanalysts and therapists encountered. She had been intrigued by the personalities of the women and was eager to delve deeper into their professional and personal challenges and concerns. She was unaware of what lay ahead for them as a group. It was Saturday morning, and she was here with them.

'Good morning. I'd like to start with just a brief check-in around what you are bringing with you to our session today, your feelings and thoughts about your work and your life and perhaps a sense of what is of central concern to you right now. Who'd like to start?'

Gabrielle, the strains of her work creasing her brow, desperately needed to share with the group. She had been looking forward to their meeting all week and was beginning to understand the power of group supervision to support her in her professional struggles. 'I think I need to start.' She looked at Tess, her eyes troubled, and then looked down. 'Things are pretty bad for me right now and I can't seem to get a handle on it.' The other women waited in silent support of what Gabi needed to say. 'I think you all know what is happening for me at work these days. It's getting worse since my sleeping has been so bad. I'm wondering what I'm going to do because it feels like I'm stuck, stuck. I've talked to my supervisor about changing the way we do business and not promoting weight loss for our patients, but she just is unwilling to budge in her approach. It's awful, so awful now. I don't even want to go there. Thank God, it's only half time, but they are talking about expanding it to full time because they are doing so much more research on weight loss and … I just can't bear the thought of having to participate in that mess. I just can't bear it.'

Gabi took a breath, and that allowed for the others to take in what she had shared with the group. Carly asked, 'Typically, I would just continue with a check-in, but I'm wondering if we can spend some time exploring this right now and then return to others afterwards? Would that be alright?' The other women nodded and Carly continued, turning again to Gabi to ask, 'Gabrielle, what is it that troubles you most about this situation?'

Gabi thought for a moment then responded, 'I just don't feel comfortable with my role in this. Patients are feeling so fearful about their health, worried about another heart attack, and I think I'm feeling guilty about my part in that. I mean, I don't support the message that they have to lose weight or else, but I'm there, I'm working with people who do advocate that. And what if I resist the message, contradict it? It sometimes seems that the mixed signals will only confuse people who are already hugely stressed and fearful.'

'Share with me more about the guilt you feel. When you talk of your work, where in your physical body do you notice tension, tightness? Where does the guilt reside?'

'Oh, I feel it here, right here.' Gabi placed both her hands on her chest. 'It's like a tightness here, a weight. Sometimes it's so bad, I can't get a proper breath and I have to just leave the room, just leave.'

'And how do you understand the guilt?'

'When I became a dietitian, I really wanted to help people, and it has just become harder and harder, not because of the patients themselves, but because of the system – the doctors and the system. The hospital where I work, they benefit from having the money to do the research with Xenical, and it's just a big machine. I've never looked at it the same since I heard my colleague Renny talk about the dangers of dieting – I think it was like a month into doing my internship. She came in to this room filled with physicians, and then she just shared study after study after study about how bad it was to promote weight loss. And I got the impression that these docs weren't expecting that at all. It was great, so inspiring. And that really shifted things for me. Transformative, really. Ever since then it has been a struggle cause I see things I didn't see before. That was definitely a turning point for me.'

'So, the guilt that you feel is that somehow also about unmet expectations?'

'Um, maybe. I guess when I was a student, I just loved my community nutrition classes. I took two of them actually at the University of Saskatchewan. One was kind of open-ended. We formed two teams and designed a community-based project, and I loved it. I loved it. I guess from that class, I started to have a perception of what a dietitian did, what kind of difference I could make in people's lives. And the reality of my work is just so different. There's a separation, and I feel at a loss to understand how I got here, how my expectations were derailed from what I imagined it would be like.' Gabi's gaze returned to the floor.

Carly, calm and intent, 'Would you say you're grieving?'

'Hmmm. I never thought of it like that, but it sure feels like grieving. Except there's no acknowledgment of grief, of loss, so it's all just in my head and it's making a mess of me and my work.'

'Gabrielle, what do you need to surrender, to release, to move through this process? Let's call it grieving for now. What is it that will open things up for you?'

'I think I need to find a new job.' As Gabi said this, her eyes cast downward.

'What does it mean for you to consider finding a new job?' The other women were listening attentively to Carly's questions, wondering themselves how they might respond.

'I feel terrible admitting this, but it feels like giving up somehow. Like I have to stay and prove something, like I'm abandoning my patients, like I'm just turning my back on them.'

Ariana, in a soft, compassionate voice, 'That is the hardest part, isn't it? Your commitment to your work and your passion for it and the impossibility of staying, of being whole.'

'Yes, it's the hardest part. I never thought I would ever have to think about leaving a job that I love so much, people that I care about. It's so hard.'

'As the object goes, so goes the source of love,' mused Jacqui. 'I'm reading Judith Butler's *The Psychic Life of Power*. She explains subject formation by combining poststructuralist and psychoanalytic theories – linking the theory of power with a theory of the psyche. I hear your lament in her writing, Gabi.'

Carly leaned forward, interested to pick up on the psychoanalytic thread, 'What I hear in Gabi's lament is perhaps ambivalence. Gabi, I'd be very curious to know if my observation resonates for you? Let's see … if you are passionate about your work, of which I have no doubt, you are perhaps defined in many ways by that same work. In this way, you might permit me to agree with Jacqui and suggest that your work could be considered an object of your love, of your desire. You are vulnerable to that object and easily exploitable by it. If the work itself is wrought with structures, seemingly abusive, regulatory power structures, then you are, in effect, subjected to that power, and since it is a power exercised by an object you desire, you find yourself perhaps submitting to that power in your desire. I would be curious about these connections given your expressions of guilt, self-beratement, grief, and inevitable melancholy if your grief remains unresolved, incomplete. Are these the markers of your subjectivity as a dietitian?' Carly paused in her question to let Gabi and the others respond.

Gabi looked perplexed. 'You know, the thought just crossed my mind that my job is rather patriarchal in many respects. I look to that work to take care of my needs while my own desires, as you call them, are disappeared. Hmmm. I'll have to think more about that one for sure. I think the theoretical turn has caused me to feel disembodied. I'm quite detached from my sadness right now. Not sure that's really helpful.' Gabi's voice trailed off and left a silent space in the room.

Tess replied, 'I don't know if this is what you were implying, Gabi, but I feel a little lost right now, too. Maybe we could do a little round and see where that takes the discussion. I want to support Gabi, but I find myself a little overwhelmed by talk of post-this and psycho-that. Sorry.'

'No need to apologize. That is a very good idea. Ariana, could you start this time?'

Carly leaned back in her chair, content to make her offering and see how it manifested in future conversations. Jacqui was at once bewitched by Carly's use of psychoanalytic language and beguiled by the divergent wishes of her colleagues. When she spoke of Gabi's ambivalence, Jacqui heard Carly's passion. If Jacqui had her way, they would explore the profession-as-patriarch symbol much further. But, like Gabi, this awareness presented an opportunity for deep reflection. For this, Jacqui was only grateful and inspired. She turned her attention back to Ariana, who started to share, in signature melodic fashion, her own misgivings with work, her description of a supervisor who was intent on having Ariana manage her time more effectively. Jacqui watched Ariana carefully, curious about the attraction she was observing between Ariana and Carly. The desire seemed to have subsumed, or had it merely been subjected? Maybe another question for Judith.

Chapter Seven – Chalk Outlines

Embodied ways, fleshy ways, the bounce and bump
and muddy squishes that we educate children out of,
teaching them as we do to climb up into their heads
and join our frightened numbers, our sad enumerations.
The Earth becomes mathematized and things
don't quite add up any more.

(Jardine, 1998, p. 140)

Week 7: October 19

Tess arrived early to class and, after arranging her notes and other paraphernalia on her table, she picked up the chalk and wrote on the board, 'Is the scientific method meeting our needs' (Buchanan, 2004)? Standing back to assess the impact of Buchanan's words, she turned, satisfied today's class had a chance of proceeding well, and she once again reviewed her ideas in preparation for the arrival of her students.

In binary fashion, Tess had come up with the idea of a debate. One side would assume the role of supporters of the scientific model and the other, the humanistic model. Of course, Tess had her biases, and she lived her contradictions within those biases. She hoped the debate structure would reveal both the biases and the contradictions. That was the hope. Time would tell how close she would get to her pedagogical ideal.

Underneath it all, Tess was really attempting to share with the students the notion of 'how we think about our relationships with other people' and how the scientific model didn't really permit that kind of thinking. Buchanan addressed this brilliantly in the context of nutrition education. His work was perhaps more palatable to students than was Harding's on the topic of whose science created knowledge for what purpose, for whose agenda (Harding, 1991). Tess was worried that increasingly difficult texts would only push the students further away. She sensed that it was time for something more inviting. It was time to ease up on the theory just a little so that the students could have a space to reflect on the ideas presented in earlier articles.

Tess thought back to her undergraduate degree and wished she had had a course about the humanistic model in nutrition research. When she was a student, there was no mention of qualitative research, no mentorship around learning of the social sciences. Even a course on conflict resolution would have been helpful. She recently attended an event about dealing with difficult people, called 'Never Fight with a Pig Because You Both Get Dirty and the Pig Enjoys It!' A smile played across Tess's mouth as she remembered that event. During the workshop the facilitator asked, 'So you think you're dealing with difficult people, but could it possibly be that you are the difficult person?' That question drew Tess up a little straighter, asked her to think about her relationships with others. She wished she had been asked to consider that question earlier in her education. She did remember a class on organizational behaviour – the biggest waste of time – she could not have taken a worse course, except that it was required for all dietetics students. She had no choice. If only that course had been about conflict resolution, effective communication between professionals, and identifying who we are and what makes us tick. If only.

Three years ago, Tess made a very difficult decision. She left the intensive care unit where she had been working for ten years. She left, quit, resigned. Perhaps it was because her father was dying and it was so real for her and she thought, 'You know what, I can no longer be part of the process that doesn't allow people to die with dignity. I can't be part of that.' She tried to change the way she looked at it, but it was futile, so she had to leave. Tess quickly realized that she couldn't influence change in the ICU because she was just the dietitian. She had no real power. She did not relish the memory of quitting. It just wasn't her style to walk away. She thought of what Gabi shared during their last supervision group, the notion of hating to give up, of not wanting to abandon all that she had contributed over the past decade. Tess could certainly relate. Three years later, Tess still had not reconciled herself to her decision; she was still unhappy that she had left, even though she acknowledged that, at the time, she had felt completely drained. For months, Tess didn't communicate the emotional loss entailed in quitting, but eventually she met with the nursing director, the medical director, and some of the nursing staff and told them exactly her reasons for leaving the unit. Her intention was to perhaps shed light on the problems so others wouldn't experience what she had. Like Buchanan, Tess wanted to emphasize the importance of relationships, of process, and of healing the healers.

It continued to be vitally important to Tess to remember that her work as a dietitian – now in community and clinical practice – was always to be in service of the patient. When she looked to her colleagues, it seemed that some of them had lost sight of that. She would never forget the experience of being with her mother in medical imaging when she had to get a central line. It was not long after her kidney transplant, and she wasn't doing well and needed some extra nutritional support. It was strange for Tess to be an observer, an onlooker, while at the same time a seasoned clinician dealing with TPN and central lines with her own patients. When Tess met her mom after the procedure, she noticed that she was crying. Tess could still recall the conversation they had that day.

'What's wrong, mom?'

'It hurts.'

'What do you mean, it hurts?'

'I felt them suturing me.'

Tess was shocked. There was absolutely no way that her mother should have felt them suturing her. Tess immediately summoned a nurse and asked to speak to the radiologist who performed the procedure. Over the phone Tess asked, 'Why is my mother in pain?'

'Well, we followed the policy.'

'My mother felt you suturing her.'

'Well, that's not possible. We followed due process. We followed the policy.'

'My mother felt you suturing her.'

'Well, we anaesthetized the area.'

'You're not hearing what I'm saying.'

'We followed the policy.'

'Maybe you need to look at the policy. You took an oath to do no harm. Today you did harm. The policy is there to deal with the majority of situations. Do you not have the ability to look at your patients to see signs of pain? I know that you do. You're a health care professional. That's why you are here.'

'We followed the policy.'

'If you fucking say that to me one more time, I don't know what I'm going to do.' Tess remembered being livid at the physician's deflecting techniques. Instead of placating her and making her go away, his comments only made her more tenacious. She remembered asking herself, 'What do I want him to do?' Then she told him, 'Let me tell you what I need. I need you to come up here and apologize to my mother and I need you to explain to her why she's in pain and more importantly, I need you to articulate to her what you are going to do to prevent this from happening to another patient.'

Tess still felt empowered by that moment. She was able to ask for exactly what she wanted in a clear and uncompromising way even though she was completely distraught that this could have happened to her dear mother. She often wondered how many others had gone through similar experiences and had not been able to assert themselves in the wake of white coats, closed doors, and unnameable indoctrination. In that moment, she felt satisfied to be an advocate for those patients and their families. She recalled how the doctor came up to the ward immediately, apologizing as he walked toward them through the swinging doors.

'You need to stop talking and start listening. This is not about you. This is about my mother.'

Her mother asked him, 'How come you didn't know I was in pain.'

'We followed the policy.'

Tess looked over at him and thought about how likely she would be to get away with slapping him across the face. 'Your policy needs to be changed. Your procedure needs to be changed if it allows people to experience pain unnecessarily.'

He finally acquiesced, 'Well, everybody was tired – everybody was running late, no coffee breaks.'

Tess couldn't believe her ears. 'You know what, I hear you, but you are making excuses. We don't want excuses. We simply want you to tell us what you are going to do to not let this happen again. That's all we want. We just don't want anybody else to suffer.'

He didn't say anything.

'Silence is not an answer.' In that moment, Tess felt tired and disillusioned, completely dissatisfied. Her only consolation was that she had made it clear to him that he had done harm. She looked him straight in the eyes and told him that, in his soul, this was not why he was a physician, beseeching him to understand. Something was missing for him that day. The lesson for Tess in that experience was the question she asked herself in reflection, 'How many times have I been part of a process that's been that way?' It was humbling for her. She felt unhinged somehow after that experience, like all her knowledge of appropriate medical practice and all her experience in clinical settings had not provided her with the power to ensure her mother's safety. She felt powerless. And in that powerlessness, an enormous sense of guilt. How could the medical system so utterly fail her mother. How could a system, one that provided Tess with her livelihood, one that Tess worked within so diligently, how could that system, that institution, inflict that much pain?

Tess's emotional wounds had healed somewhat from the experience, but still she felt a tender ache, familiar in her chest. Her sense of fairness and justice provoked, leaving that spot in her chest always a little raw, biting. This was also what fired her desire for ethical dietetic practice, for always doing right by her patients. And it was with this desire that she offered the Buchanan article, wanting to say, 'Look! Look at what science does to people! Look at the pain that is done in the name of science! And, now look hard for alternatives.' Like Muriel Rukeyser asking her readers to *hold a mirror up to our histories*. Who will not be implicated in this practice we call science when we hold a mirror up to our histories? Tess imagined that mirror before her eyes suddenly shattering with the thoughts of what she did to patients early in her career. She sought redemption and reconciliation for those artless transgressions. She knew better now, and she attempted to construe her agency by teaching the dietetic students a different way, by initiating them in a manner that fostered continuity between theory and practice, between the heightened expectations and the myriad realities of dietetics. This was her hope, her desire. It was the least she could perform. She used that experience as a reminder to her to follow her gut, to trust her intuition, and to listen to her heart – all of which were not encouraged in a clinical nutrition text. That was why the Buchanan article was so important to Tess. She wanted to believe that dietitians had more power than they thought, but that was not how they were prepared to come to their work whether it was in clinical or community settings. She wondered about the impact of a healing touch – a touch that was the antithesis of what she had been taught to promote as a clinician-educator. She thought about what negative interpersonal energy did to patients, did to her patients in that ICU. How could it possibly promote healing and wellness? It led to caustic relationships. What was it about the scientific method that obliterated the relational, the human dimension? Tess intended to bring these questions to the surface with her students by using Buchanan's text as an exemplar. She would ask the students, 'Was the scientific method meeting their needs?'

꙳

'I'm so mad right now, I could scream!'

Jacqui was reading an e-mail message from Tess. Both of them, along with all the other dietitians in Canada, had received a message from their national association sent in response to recent research that suggested deaths attributable to obesity and overweight had been overestimated in the past. The broadcast e-mail insisted that despite the revised statistics, dietitians should continue to promote weight loss for those who were overweight and obese. The message deeply offended Jacqui and those of her colleagues who had a radically different view of the issue. They discovered a long time ago that it wasn't really what people weighed, it was how active they were that determined their risk for early death and disease. Jacqui had been embroiled in a long-standing debate around this issue with the national association. Receiving the e-mail was like being poked in the eye with a stick. It made her irate. She drafted a reply – copying it to Tess, Ariana, and Gabrielle, her most ardent supporters – asking the association to provide references in support of its position. The association did not respond. She sent another message. A response came, asking her to move her concerns to a web-based discussion board so that all dietitians could participate. Jacqui felt silenced and brushed off, but no less irritated.

'I can't believe they want you to use that stupid discussion board. It's just ridiculous,' Tess wrote. 'I'm just drafting my message now, but I have to calm down first. This is just so out of hand what they have done here.'

Jacqui felt a small measure of relief knowing that she was not the only one who was outraged. This comfort of comradeship enabled her to focus more intently on her reply to the national association, like a little breeze blowing away the morning fog. She could see clearly.

Her letter began:

I'm deeply concerned with the content of the backgrounder you sent to all members. In effect, you are saying that dietitians, the most trusted source of information on the science of nutrition, should ignore the emerging science that has been presented to us by Flegal et al. (2005). I've been making this point over and over for several years now in many different professional contexts and communications. When I read blatantly erroneous and biased information of the variety you have presented as fact to members, I feel a sense of unease, a profound sense of unease. I believe your intentions are to ensure that the good work of dietitians continues to support the health of Canadians. Instead, this information promotes fat discrimination, oppression, and shaming. We are doing harm when we practise dietetics in a way that promotes weight loss for all those whose body mass index is above 25. It is wrong. Anyone who is aware of the data refuting the claims you have shared would be outraged. But I suspect, as usual, I'm the only one who has raised this as a concern. And, as usual, I suspect nothing will be done. I've decided not to post anything to the discussion board, as this is tantamount to pushing my concerns to the margins of debate. I'm still at a loss as to where the information you shared is cited. There are no references. It seems you are asking me to accept those statements as truth claims. I will not do it.

Knowing that it was a strongly worded message, Jacqui decided not to send it right away, but to leave it in her 'drafts' folder until the morning. She had a hard time sleeping that night. So many thoughts spun through her head. The most pressing being, 'You should just quit this profession. Just quit. Walk away. Relieve yourself of this angst. You have a choice. Choose not to engage in this madness.' And then, a tempered response, 'If you were to leave now, all your research into the experience of dietetic education and possibilities for change would be for naught. If you're not a member of the profession, why would the profession listen to you about your research? You need your job. You can't work without the insurance you get so inexpensively by being a member of the association. You are trapped. You have no choice. Maybe you can make a difference. Eventually, your work will reach the right person, and changes to the way dietitians are educated will be made. Don't give up.' And then a third voice, tempered by years of therapy. 'Why are you so self-righteous? Why so angry? You don't have to respond like this. You are not a victim. Remember your power, your inner flow.' It was this maddening debate that kept Jacqui fully awake until 1:30, when she heard Evyn call for her nighttime feeding. Jacqui carefully got out of bed so as to not disturb Kelly and made her way to the kitchen to warm Evyn's bottle. Feeding Evyn was a welcomed distraction. As she picked her up and rubbed her warm back, thoughts of professional associations vanished, and Jacqui was deeply present with the sleepy, hungry soul of another.

ે♣

'Hi, Tess. Is now still a good time to talk?' Dani felt awkward now. It was much easier to complain to Dr Taylor about Tess than to speak to Tess directly.

'Yep. Come in.' Because she didn't have a space of her own, Tess had borrowed an office to meet with Dani. The shelves were lined with nutrition journals of every variety, certainly not the reading material Tess preferred. Thankfully, she was not here to read. Dani entered, closed the door, and sat in one of the chairs facing Tess. Tess felt the seriousness of their meeting accelerate with the closing of the door. Perhaps she should ask Dani to leave it open, but maybe she had something personal that she wanted to share with Tess.

'What's on your mind, Dani?'

Dani could tell from the look on Tess's face that what she was about to say would come as a surprise. She almost reconsidered. 'Yeah, well, anyway, I just need to give you some feedback about the course.'

'Hmmm. Go ahead, yes. Feedback is great.'

'I was pretty surprised at my mark on our first assignment. I was sure I had done exactly what you requested of us. Well ... I really don't think that the information we are covering has any real use to us as dietitians. It's just, well, it's a waste of time.'

'Oh.'

'I spoke with Dr Taylor about it and she said I should tell you, too. I just wish we could cover more stuff that was important, and it just seems like you are making it up as we go. I mean, there are no learning objectives, so how are we supposed to know what to learn?' Dani was letting it all slip out now. Tess sat back in her chair. Her smile faded.

'I realize that the readings may seem a bit obscure, Dani. Part of what you may be responding to is my teaching style and that's fine. And part of it may be the strangeness of the content. Would you say that's a fair assessment?'

'No, it's just, you know, what's the point? How is this theory stuff even remotely related to being a dietitian? I go in, I share my nutrition knowledge, and that's it. Done. What difference does it make whether I work from the science model or whatever? I just don't see the relevance really.'

'Dani, it might be hard to put the connections together right now, but I ask that you give it some time. Just try to stay open and see what happens. Actually, your questions remind me of my colleague, Jacqui. She is coming in for a class next month. She wrote a chapter about a course she took as a dietetic undergrad and she had a very similar response to you, I think. Now, what was it called? Something to the effect of 'Like Cold Water or a Kiss,' yeah, something kind of off-beat. I have the book here' (Gingras, 2004). Tess reached in her bag for the book Jacqui had given to her to read during their last cup of tea together. 'It's actually Jacqui's copy, but I don't think she'd mind me lending it to you. Just bring it to class next week. You might even want to ask Jacqui about it when she joins us. Now, I haven't read the entire thing, but I think your experience may be very similar to hers. I invite you to give it a read and then let's meet again after next class. Would that be OK?'

Dani looked at the book's title – *Home Economics Now: Transformative Practice, Ecology, and Everyday Life*. 'But this is about home economics.'

'Yes, it is. Dietetics originated from home ec.'

'I didn't realize that. So, you want me to read this article?' Dani sounded entirely sceptical.

'I think that would be a good start. Let's meet again next week after class. I want to know what you think about Jacqui's experience. And do you have your assignment with you? I'd like to take a look at it to remind myself of how I marked it.'

Dani pulled out her assignment, which now looked a little dishevelled. They spent the next fifteen minutes going over Dani's work. Afterwards Dani had a much better sense of what Tess was looking for in terms of ideas. Tess even decided to increase her mark modestly after getting a clearer understanding of Dani's perspective on the assignment – an understanding that could only come from talking to her face to face. The text – any text – constrained at times, hobbled understanding, handcuffed the reader and writer. Tess understood these marks were vitally important to undergraduates, and she also understood how that had come to be. Marks and the overemphasis on their importance were just another part of a structure that objectified students, quantified their humanity. Tess wished it was less so, but she also realized that she didn't have the energy or the time to do anything to change it.

Once Dani left, Tess reflected on the chain of events that Dani had put into play through her conversation with Alice. Tess wondered when or if she would be hearing from Alice. She tried not to think too much about the implications, the consequences of doing what she was doing pedagogically. Tess knew that her intentions were sound and defensible even though she didn't relish the thought of having to defend those intentions. The negative thoughts were there, but she tried to ease her mind out of what was beyond her control and into the present moment. Instead, she shuddered at the thought that it might very well be the beginning of the storm. And, still six more weeks left in the term. How would she get through?

❧

'Hey, Dani.' Meg was sitting downstairs eating her lunch when Dani walked by after talking with Tess.

'Hi.' Dani made like she wasn't going to stop and talk to Meg, but she then reconsidered, needing someone to commiserate with, someone to share her distress with NUTR 430.

'What's up?' Meg asked, shifting over so Dani could sit down beside her. Meg took in the force that was Dani – her Miss Sixty jeans nonchalantly low, exposing her midriff, smooth tanned skin drawn tight across protruding hips, plush pink velour of her Juicy Couture top, zippered down, revealing a snug white Lululemon yoga cami, the pink gloss of her lips, the impossible swing of her long brown hair held back temporarily by a pair of JLo-inspired sunglasses. Meg sensed the heady pull of Dani's cultural attire. Conforming, but indifferent. Instantly, Meg felt uneasy, awkward, ugly, in her loose-fitting cargos, plain T-shirt, and comfortable shoes. She noticed her derivative desire, her impulsive need to accumulate the spectacle of Dani's ease, but Meg knew this body came at a cost.

'Oh, God! I just talked with Tess. What do you think of her?' Suddenly, Meg heard Dani's voice take on a conspiratorial tone. Meg's eyes lifted from her corporeal appraisal. Dani was accustomed to having such an effect. She was deliberate in her indifference. Her careful choice of clothes, her exhaustive regime of exercise, and her protracted starvation took an incredible amount of her time and energy. To maintain this existence, the power of being seen, there was no alternative.

'What do I think of Tess or the course?' Meg put her apple down in preparation for a defence of both.

'Well, both, I guess. I just don't … half the time I have no idea what the hell is going on in that course.'

'Yeah, it's pretty different than our other courses.' Meg was reluctant to agree with Dani, but felt certain this was a one-time invitation into Dani's approval, and perhaps her decadent inner circle. Meg understood the capital in being swept up, accepted by Dani with her throng of friends and entirely prolific social life. Meg heard all about it from one of her roommates, who partied with Dani's friends. Meg was feeling a bit of an outcast, the good girl, but unsure if she wanted it any other way. Meg said nothing further and resumed eating her apple.

Dani continued. 'I just wish she would be a little more clear about everything, anything. I did crap on my first assignment. I thought it would be easy. Sucks for us that Dr Taylor had to take a research leave this term, our last term before applying for internships. What a pain!'

As Dani got more emphatic, Meg felt her words cowering in response. She really wanted to get an internship, too. Unlike Dani, she did pretty well on the first assignment. Meg knew she should say something, but what?

'Uh, have you talked to Tess?'

'Yeah, I had to cause Dr Taylor isn't going to do anything about it.'

'What did Tess say?'

'She just sat there and then gave me this stupid chapter to read from this ridiculous home ec book. What a waste of time.'

'Oh. What are you going to do?'

'Well, I can't just blow it off, can I?' Dani was really irritated and found Meg completely unhelpful, unsupportive.

'No, I guess not. Um, yeah, I don't know.'

'Anyway, I gotta go. I guess I'll see you in class.' Dani had checked out of their conversation. She correctly assumed she would find no sympathetic accomplice in Meg. She gathered her bag, her lithe body, and made her departure, barely acknowledging Meg's reply.

'Yeah, see ya.' Meg's voice trailed off as she watched Dani leave through the front doors of their building. A familiar sense of loneliness washed over Meg. She wondered how she could be surrounded by so many people and still feel so alone? Were others feeling this way? Why did she find it so hard to connect with people?

Meg picked up her bag, threw her apple core in the garbage nearby, and left through the same doors as Dani. She decided it was time to reach out. She had been thinking about joining the women's centre on campus. She was tired of walking through life as if a ghost. It was time to explore the world outside of dietetics for a change. It was time to do something meaningful. Her spirits lifted just slightly at the promise of making a difference for someone. It was just not going to happen here, as a student in the dietetics program.

ì

October 21

Dear Judith,

It's this very notion of subjection that has me in a knot today. You ask, 'How is it, then, that the longing for subjection, based on a longing for social existence, recalling and exploiting primary dependencies, emerges as an instrument and effect of the power of subjection?' Am I to understand that in becoming a socially recognizable subject, through language, of course, I am immediately exploited by that longing, and position myself as an instrument of (self) abuse? I deem this a hermeneutical wager thus: I cannot be inside the question and outside at the same time. Who, then, asks the question in a fashion that is not constituted by the questioner's power, exploiting the question for her own purposes? The asking of the question cleverly demands an attention to the subject, who is instantly granted recognition in the very asking of the question. Thus the response to the question is irrelevant. It is the asking that matters, that determines to some significant extent ontologically, a subject wrought by some uncertain form of twisting. It is the asking that marks the subject as submissive – a mandatory submission, and at the same time, an instrument of power. It is the asking that signifies the subject's desire to be recognized and, at the same time, initiates the subject's subjection. In your words, 'the double aspect of subjection appears to lead to a vicious circle: the agency of the subject appears to be an effect of its subordination.' A referential paradox, you say: we must refer to that which does not exist.

Judith, bear with my attempts to play out the wager. Who am I that is asking and at the same time being asked? What possibility for agency exists if the question of how to resist the subordination is not asked, and, in the not asking, the subject does not reiterate its own subjection? So goes the object of desire. *As the object goes, so goes the source of love.* But there is no agency without passionate attachments, even if those attachments are destructive. Oh, you disagree. *If in acting the subject retains the conditions of its emergence, this does not imply that all of its agency remains tethered to those conditions and that those conditions remain the same in every operation of agency.* Well, as you suggest, this presupposes discontinuity between the power that initiates the subject and the power that the subject wields.

I turn my focus reflexively towards my own education as a dietitian. This, you say, *becomes the precipitating condition of subject formation, a primary longing in recoil.* And of this longing, I derive solace. But how might I describe the power of initiation as discontinuous from the power of reiteration? In the very writing of this letter, I make that enabling break between the two. I've appropriated the power that initiates so that I might use it against what makes that assumption possible. The power is altered, you insist, and is able to retain and resist that subordination. And, the agency, my agency, is bound in ambivalence.

I feel ambivalent towards my dietetic practice. I want to leave. I need to stay. Melancholia and passion. *The subject eclipses the condition of its emergence; it eclipses power with power.* I become that ambivalence – linguistically at first and then as an individual. *A theory of subject should take into account the full ambivalence of the conditions of its operation.* Have my acts already been domesticated in advance? You tell me that the subject cannot quell the ambivalence by which it is constituted – an ambivalence reiterated at the heart of agency. Painful and promising. Already-there and yet-to-come. I make myself an object for reflection, my desire is regulated, through my grief I come to understand what I can accomplish, and I reach the edge of my reflexivity. Here I am. So why do I feel so sad?

In-consolable,
Jacqui

‚â•

'I really need some support today.' Tess had needed support for some time, but her need was becoming urgent, and she couldn't ignore it any longer.

'Is that OK with others?' Carly checked in with the group before starting with Tess. She knew that one of the ways supervision was successful was if the people involved truly felt they were guiding the direction of the group. This was a skill for a facilitator, to be open yet guiding at the same time.

'I think it's really important we provide some time and space for Tess.' All heads nodded in agreement with Ariana's statement. The rest of the women sat back as Tess leaned forward and began to speak.

'I must begin by saying that the teaching is going really well. I'm loving it. Loving the chance to just offer these students something a little different. A space for them to consider what it is they're getting into. It's such a wondrous experience. And at the same time, there is resistance. I find the resistance so intense, so deafening. It scares me. I think I'm most threatened by the resistance.'

'If the resistance were a person, what would it say to you?' Carly was venturing into a dramatic space, a performing space. Tess was wary.

'Uh, mmmm. I'm not sure.'

'Try not to think, try not to analyse too carefully, Tess. See what comes out when you inhabit or personalize that resistance.' Carly reassured Tess and at the same time urged her to take a step into the unknown.

'Well, it says, "What's the point of this nonsense? We don't need to learn this stuff."'

'OK. Good. That also sounds like what some students might say. Try to really speak to the resistance, the essence of resistance as if it were a person. Give the resistance a voice.'

Tess took a breath and looked like she might refuse Carly's invitation. Instead her resistant double said, 'I'm not going to do it. I'm not. I don't feel safe learning this stuff. I don't want to know. I don't care. This isn't what my job is about. Nobody told me. Nobody warned me. I think it's ridiculous.'

Tess's usually serene demeanour was now surprisingly fiery, fierce. She stepped in fully to the resistance. She played it out.

Carly went along, 'What's so ridiculous about learning?'

Tess was contemptuous, biting, 'What's so lovely about having your entire life turned upside down and watching everything you have ever learned turned into lies? You tell me' (Lather, 1991, p. 155).

Ariana joined in. 'And what is the truth?'

Tess turned her head suddenly towards Ariana, not expecting to hear from her, yet willing to engage. 'The truth hurts, Ariana. You should know that.'

Gabi looked worried. 'This is starting to feel weird.'

'Let's play it out a little further. Remember, Tess is taking on a character. It's not Tess. It's a character Tess is playing.' Then turning away from Gabi, she directed her next pointed question to Tess's resistance character, 'Do you have a name? What do you call yourself?'

'I'm Bitch!'

'Oh, OK. So, Bitch, what do you think about Tess's teaching?'

Jacqui thought the question was taking them into frightening possibilities. Her heart began to pound in her chest. Tess was courageous, storming into the performance, deeper and deeper.

'It's bullshit.' Tess stood like she couldn't bear sitting with herself. A force in her body willed her up as an attempt to distance herself from this outlandish Bitch.

'Really? What makes you say that?'

'It's a joke. She is fooling herself if she believes she's going to mount some kind of epistemological revolution. It's a superficial, half-hearted attempt, really. It's embarrassing to be part of it.'

'Oh, so you're somehow implicated in this? For what purpose are you involved?' Carly inquired.

'Don't patronize me.' Tess spoke with uncharacteristic venom and disdain for Carly's question.

Carly was vaguely surprised with how quickly and authentically Tess had immersed herself as 'Bitch.' She made a mental note to ask her if she had ever done anything similar in the past. For now, though, Carly attempted to enlarge the cast of this performance. Looking to the other women, she asked, 'Does anyone have questions for Bitch?'

Gabi smiled nervously, but said nothing. Ariana, ever a dramatist, ventured in with her question, 'Where do you live?'

'I live here and … here.' Tess pointed instantly to her forehead and less certainly to her gut.

'How long have you lived there?'

'Too long to remember.'

Jacqui tentatively asked, 'What do you think of Tess being here in this supervision group?'

'It's fine. I'm humouring her. She insists that she wants to be here and that she likes you women for reasons I will never understand.' Tess smiled and Gabi laughed, but it was an unnatural, anxious shrill.

Ariana as devious foil, 'You're right. That kind of relationship, my friend, you will never fully understand.'

Carly was pleased with how the activity, the psychodrama, was playing out. It had raised some interesting dynamics within the group. She wanted to hear from Gabi. 'Anything to ask, Gabi?'

Gabi stammered, 'Uh, no, not really. No.' The thought of interacting with this unknown terror was too much for her to comprehend.

'I have something to say to Bitch.' Ariana, looking strangely serene, her eyes not leaving Tess, spilled her statement slowly, tenderly vying with the demon to which she was no stranger. 'I love you.'

Tess looked hard at Ariana, but said nothing.

'I love you,' Ariana repeated. 'And, I will always love you.'

Tess looked like she might respond, but the words caught in her throat. The hard edge of Bitch, the tightening of Tess's jaw, loosened, just barely perceptibly.

'Put down your weapons. Let them go. Be here with us.' Jacqui had imagined Bitch to be carrying all sorts of harming devices – knives slashing out at people, trying to keep them away, but sometimes drawing blood. And, most often, cutting Tess up from the inside.

'What do you know of these weapons?' Tess finally spoke.

'We know all too well of these weapons.' Ariana stood, tentative, her eyes still locked on Tess, took two steps forward, now immediately before her. Ariana, her diminutive and undaunted frame in sharp contrast to Tess, tall, even more giant in her dominant Bitch persona. Then Ariana carefully reached for Tess's hands and raised them to her mouth and with the most tender of motions, kissed them together and held them still to her lips.

Jacqui, Gabi, and Carly watched as Bitch softened, melted almost, in Ariana's brave embrace.

Carly carefully guided the performance to a new dimension. 'OK, Tess, just notice what is happening now in your body, in your head, in your gut. Ariana, don't move. Both of you be still and simply notice.'

After several seconds, Carly asked, 'What are you noticing now, Tess?'

Tess started to talk, but her voice caught. When she started over, she had tears streaming down her face. 'I notice a loosening, a tension, a tightness, a release of those.'

'Ariana, what are you aware of now?'

'My heart is racing. My palms are wet. God, so sorry about that, Tess.' Ariana smiled. Through her tears, Tess also smiled, waves of relief washed over them, over all of them.

Carly spoke to Tess and Ariana, 'Just stay there for another moment.' Then to Gabi and Jacqui, 'Alright, I would like the two of you to join Tess and Ariana in the making of a human sculpture.'

Jacqui immediately rose. Gabi, more reluctant, muttered, 'Huh?'

'Come on Gabi. Give it a try.' Jacqui urged, standing beside Ariana.

'Without thinking too much about what to do, simply offer the sculpture started by Tess and Ariana what you believe it needs, what they need, and what you need.' Gabi stood and joined Jacqui already trying to arrange herself somehow as a human chair for Tess to rest upon. Gabi was clearly bewildered and felt like an outcast. She stood, pondered the three, stepped back, circled, then, in an act of faith, moved in close behind Ariana, and offered her hands as a support to Ariana's elbows. Ariana rested her arms in Gabi's open palms.

'Wow!' Carly finally stood. 'Magnificent! OK, I'm going to touch each of you one at a time and I want you to say the first word that comes to mind.' Carly bent to touch Jacqui's shoulder.

'Willing.'

Carly moved around to touch Gabi. 'Perplexed.'

Tess. 'Disoriented.'

Ariana. 'Relieved.'

Carly slowly repeated each word, offering them back to the women, 'Relieved, disoriented, willing, perplexed. Relieved, disoriented, willing, perplexed. Such lovely contradictions. OK, carefully disengage with the sculpture, but continue to attend to your innermost thoughts and feelings and quietly take your seats.'

The women extricated themselves from the sculpture and dutifully returned to their chairs and took a collective breath. Carly was busy gathering paper and pens out of her tawny leather attaché. She began to distribute these to each of the women.

'OK. That was most stunning. I would like to dedicate the next ten minutes to free writing. Just put pen to paper and let the words flow. Do not lift that pen! Then we'll close today's session with a checkout, and you can share some of what you wrote, too. Sound OK?'

Jacqui was already busy writing, questions flooded her thoughts, pen whirled into response. She wrote, 'What is the resistance that we all have living within us? How might we love her? Who among us is brave enough to say those first loving utterances? In all my heart, I was fearful of that Bitch, the stranger unknown to me, yet the way we see the other is connected to the way we see ourselves. The other is ourselves as the stranger' (Okri, 1997). She wrote and wrote, thirsty for words, leaning on Ben Okri, his text springing forward to support her questions. Was she other to herself? Her writing had her in flight and all at once her heart was full.

ஃ

Since the beginning of her research, Jacqui had been preoccupied with the question of what it was that dietitians do. During the second research workshop, much to her delight, the conversation turned to this particular topic. Michelle said, 'Well I talk about food!' Nancy explained that she teaches people how to eat healthy. 'At least that's what I tell my kids!' After these light-hearted responses, the conversation took a more serious tone. Corine stated soberly, 'I'm not convinced we really know what works. I've been caught up over the years in defending what I do. We need outward recognition cause something inside is lacking. And is it because we don't know who we are and what our worth is as dietitians?' Corine's question was met with only silence.

Corine spoke again, this time more vehemently. 'What is our role – I'd like to see what we can agree on as a group? What is the broadest and most general statement about our role? Because I'm not convinced we know.'

Jacqui wondered aloud, 'Can our role be defined like that? Is there a collective story about what it is that we do? I'm not sure such a thing exists.'

Pauline had brought as her artefact the *Core Competencies for Health Promoters* from the University of Toronto's Health Promotion Program. 'These core competencies lean more towards the kind of work I'm doing now, but they're not competencies I gained through my education. Definitely again my work experience is leading me away from believing there are contributions unique to dietitians.'

Angela remarked about the defensiveness in their posture. 'We can't help people change their behaviour. Like many physicians, we're going through an existential identity crisis. They can't help people change their behaviour either, which is why they're defending their territory so powerfully. We are trying to defend our territory, too, but we don't have as much power and there are fewer of us doing it.' She paused before adding, 'We're powerless at helping people change their behaviour. We don't have the skills to facilitate that process.'

Jacqui listened to this exchange over and over, noticing how these women's conversations about food and teaching others about food had turned to serious admissions of their powerlessness and how this perhaps coincided with an identity crisis. She wondered how they had been *educated into their heads, their sad enumerations*, and out of embodied ways of being dietitians. Could such a being exist – dietitian being instead of dietitian doing? According to her colleagues, dietitian being was an experience worth considering *since things didn't quite add up anymore.*

Chapter Eight – Quiet Still

Suggestions, possibilities, provocations, hints, and hopes and glancing blows luring our speech out into the open.

(Jardine, 1998, p. 139)

Tess was rushing that morning. Her insistence that class start on time was going to make a hypocrite of her. Too much. She had been trying to do too much. Thinking she had lots of time, she had lingered over the newspaper, becoming lost in memories of her group supervision experience and feelings of vulnerability. How could she have said those things? Before she realized the time, Zoë had bounded downstairs, desperate to have a shirt button reattached, and Michael, in his dismal attempts to prepare breakfast, had started the smoke detector by burning the toast. Calm to chaos in sixty seconds. She escaped the madness relatively unscathed and dropped Zoë off at school, insisting all the while that car rides to school were not to be expected in the future. She remembered Zoë's laughter as she slammed her door and parted with, 'Yeah, right, mom. Whatever.'

Now, Tess was run-walking from the parkade to the class. Her dress, coat, and scarf all flared out in her wake, while the fine mist of rain reminded Tess of her forgotten umbrella. What a mess! As she breezed into the room, she immediately noticed the quiet. And then she realized why. Alice was sitting in a chair in the far front corner. Tess's heart skipped a beat.

'Good morning, Tess. Glad you could join us.' Alice was attempting some sort of brandishing humour. Tess felt humiliated and undone.

'Well, what a lovely surprise.' Tess drew herself up, attempting to recapture some semblance of composure. 'To what do we owe the honour of your presence, Dr Taylor?'

The students were visibly intrigued by the exchange, noticeably silent, like recalcitrant children in the room with bickering parents – suddenly sweet, precious, angelic. Tess looked around the room and met their gazes while removing her coat and smoothing her dress. She attempted to smooth her worry and anxiety as well, but those feelings persisted.

'I've been meaning to drop by for sometime and when my meeting was cancelled this morning, I thought, wonderful, I'll sit in with you. My good fortune.'

Tess, mouth dry, still slightly breathless, wished they weren't having this exchange in front of the students. She felt entirely exposed. It was a defining moment. How might she proceed?

'Our good fortune, really.' Tess attempted a smile. She was sure the students could read through its plasticity. Tess quickly thought about what they would be discussing for today's class. Oh, God! The ethics of authenticity. Great. Tess began a silent inner monologue. 'OK, breathe. Put down your weapons. Step into your creativity. Embrace resistance. She is sitting right here with all of you. Love her. Love her fiercely.'

'Alright everyone, I'd like to spend most of today's class discussing Martinez's article. How about we arrange ourselves into groups of three, and, Dr. Taylor, you can join in, too, as will I, like before. Let's spend about fifteen minutes just getting a sense from each other what the article is about, what Martinez is trying to say, and then come up with one question we could ask Martinez as if he were actually here. OK? So, there should be about ten questions for you to share with the class. Each group will write their question on the board, and then we will spend the next fifteen minutes attempting a collective response, back in our same groups. So, groups of three. I'll let you know when fifteen minutes is up.' Tess immediately joined with two students and asked them what they thought about the article. She was obliquely aware that Alice was looking around to find herself a group. Everyone else was gratefully busy. For once, Tess found the students' chatter a welcome distraction.

Dani was entirely astounded at this turn of events. She had

complained to Dr Taylor about Tess, and, the very next class, Dr Taylor shows up. Wild! She had loved the pained expression on Tess's face when she walked in and saw Dr Taylor. But now, it seemed that the fun was over. Too bad. She glanced over to the student closest to her, motioning her to form a group of two. Dani noticed Dr Taylor wasn't in a group yet. It would be too weird to join with her. Just then, Dr Taylor joined with Meg's group, which caused Dani to feel vexed. Frustrated, she turned her attention to a third student milling about the class and impatiently waved her over. Dani attempted to move a desk to make room for her two group mates and accidentally dropped her copy of the article. The pages splayed open. Grabbing it by the staple, she noticed for the first time a quote from an anonymous medical student appearing on an otherwise blank page. '*We are learning when you least expect it.*' You've got to be kidding me, she thought. Whatever.

After fifteen minutes, Tess excused herself from the two others in her group and stood to address the class. 'Alright, let's start getting those questions up on the board.'

Last-minute suggestions and edits were negotiated, and students filed up to the front of the room. Chalk in hand, the students wrote their questions, some borrowed directly from the author's own wonderings.

'What should students do if they feel morally traumatized?'

'How can dietetic students resolve conflict in a direction that fosters integrity?'

'What does the author mean by "The intrinsic values and the activities of professions define the profession"?'

'What happens when institutions and individuals are not united in moral priorities?'

'What happens when student goals and university goals are different?'

'How does the medical/dietetic educational process encourage the creation of artificial persons?'

'What changes are required for a view of professional role to include responsibilities of identifying and criticizing institutional moral failure?'

'What is the performance of a dietitian in the health care theatre?'

'What boundaries should we be aware of in dietetic practice?'

'What elements are necessary for integrity?'

While Tess watched the students write their questions on the board, she noticed how comfortable she was beginning to feel with the prospect of discussing these complex, ethical concepts. These ideas were important to her, and it was in the possibility of sharing some of her thoughts on the ethics of authenticity that Tess's heart began to find its natural rhythm. Her mouth moistened in preparation for speech.

'Wonderful, excellent questions. All of them. OK, now if you could reconvene with your same group, I will number you off, one to ten. Work together to prepare a response to the question that corresponds to your group number. And it's OK if you are in a group working on a question that you created.'

After assigning numbers, Tess sat down with a new group. They were assigned question number six, 'How does the medical/dietetic educational process encourage the creation of artificial persons?'

Her group members were cautious at first. Then, once the ideas began to flow unimpeded, they energetically took up the task of understanding an artificial person. Tess enjoyed herself in the task and was surprised when a student from another group told her it was time to stop. There were only five minutes left in the class.

'Oh! OK. Please nominate a scribe in your group to post the question and your response to Blackboard. Please post these within the next two days, and I will read all of them before our next class. I'll make some final remarks and maybe ask some additional questions of Martinez then as well. Everyone have a scribe?' Heads nodded. 'Great.' The students made that instant rush to leave. Tess pre-empted their exit.

'Two final things before we finish. First, we are now into the second half of the course. You've had one assignment marked and, I hope, three reader responses handed in. I would like to dedicate the first ten minutes of our next class to your half-way feedback, so give some thought to what you would like to share with me about that. Second, since we took up our second or third class with Amy's story, I've decided to combine the readings for week nine and ten. Don't worry – you've already read Travers's piece and the other reading is relatively short. So, next week it's Jacqui's "trust" article, and on November 9th we'll be discussing Gussow and revisiting Travers. I'll also put that announcement on Blackboard for a reminder. Then on November 16th Jacqui will be here to talk about her recent research on dietitian identity, which merges well with Martinez's article actually. Lots of connections. Any questions about that?'

'And our second assignment is due when?'

'Right, second and final assignment is also due on November 16th.'

Tess wondered how Alice was interpreting her patchwork but tried not to let her concerns intensify. She felt vindicated somehow for how the class started. As the students filed out of the room, Alice approached.

'Well, that was fun. I really enjoyed that, Tess. Thanks. You are a really great facilitator. I've never really had so much group work during a lecture before.'

Tess heard less than flattering tones in Alice's remarks but decided to accept them at face value.

'You're welcome. I'm glad you could come and get a better sense of what we're up to here. I'm enjoying it immensely.'

'Great. Glad to hear it. Say, has Dani been to talk to you lately?'

'Yes, yes, we just spoke last week.'

'She seems a little concerned about things, about how things are going for her in this class.'

'Um-hm.' Tess was reluctant to volunteer details of their discussion. Instead she shared that Dani was a very bright, articulate presence in the class and the other students benefited immensely from her scepticism.

Alice listened and agreed with her assessment. Seemingly reassured that all was right, Alice excused herself to attend to the multitude of tasks and duties that awaited her attention.

Tess, weary, gathered her belongings and felt the weight of her conscience. She turned off the lights and closed the door. With that small click, she realized without a doubt that the storm was upon her, and in the quiet walk back to her car she attempted to regain her bearings before the next gale blasted her sails. Shivering now, first hot then cold, Tess wondered how she might have made it through that class had it not been for her dramatic performance in group supervision only four days earlier – the release of her attachment to others' resistance, which also revealed her own dark force of resistance rooted in her mind and her gut. The activity had provided a clear space for her to maintain her own pedagogic integrity. The tension might otherwise have been too much for her to contain. Perfect timing. She was unable to explain the serendipity of it all. Of course, these everyday mysteries were better left unscrutinized.

ও

October 30

Dear Judith,

I think I need to take a break from our correspondence. It has caused me to start sounding like a pretentious ass. I believe what I need right now is a poem and the excess of its disruptive promise, as you say (Butler, 1991, p. 29). I will write soon. Until then ...

In-effective,
Jacqui

ও

Ariana was running, as she often did. Just her, alone on a muddy trail, the early morning mist stifling what little noise she was creating; pounding of feet, breath, house key on her shoelace. The mist and the quiet invited her mind to drift, to pick up loose strands of subconscious, like delicately picking one pearl on a strand and lifting that strand out of a box of pearls and jewels, a milky delicacy of thought lifted forth, through the mist. The last supervision meeting. It was curious. What possessed her to stand and offer herself to Tess's Bitch that way, humbled and innocent? Why her? A small grade claimed her focus; more breath, surging legs pushed, up up. Little slip. Oh. Momentum up. There. Ah, stride lengthened. Freely. Her thoughts wandered back to supervision. She thought of shame. She placed a 'shame' slide under a microscope, took a closer look. Shame. Healing their shame. The group of them. Shame from comparing, always falling short of their expectations, shaming others. Weight. Feeling bad about others' poor comportment, their indiscretions, their sheer lack of will. Undisciplined. Ignore that they could still be healthy, ignore the research that says fat is not going to kill, turn your face away, just plough on, plough over people, help them in spite of themselves. That's their inadequacy, not ours. We shame. Ours mixes with theirs, the others. Othering is shaming. No chance to heal. Confusion. Sharper corners in the trail, she swerved, faster downhill. Breath, wind, quickened in quiet mist. What was needed, collectively, to heal? To name that wound first, maybe? Say it out loud. Ariana heard her faint voice rehearsing, 'I'm ashamed.' No, she wouldn't want to do that. But she could write poems, enough to fill oceans, poems about shame. She wrote volumes of poems in her standing to face Tess. Not even thinking. Just standing. Just their two hearts, Ariana's plump with crimson and Tess's Bitch heart, shrunken, withered. A heart of contempt. She wanted their hearts to meet. I love you. Without thinking, just feeling. I love you. Wonder what Carly thought? Yeah. Carly. God, what a splendid distraction! Everything about Carly – the coolness, grace, intensity. Ariana slowed her pace, imperceptibly,

coming abreast of Carly now. Oh, yes. Aware of her own growing fascination, Ariana trembled, shivered, ran from it, ran faster.
Could that be spoken? Ariana whispering, 'Carly.' Wrapping her
lips around the word, 'Carly, Carly.' Now, just Carly and the
seduction of private thoughts. No Tess. No Bitch. No shame.
Just Ariana running with Carly, indelibly connected, running
through mist and quiet and snap of twig, but no one to hear
them. Running home, running to herself. Running through mist
and desire. Running fast. And still, the quiet.

⁂

Ariana, home from her run, needed to clear her mind of Carly
by writing through it. In a restless, climactic bout of writing,
she articulated her intense attraction. Lines upon lines of words
spilled onto pages. She wrote her desire empty, which she had to
do. Ariana understood her attraction to Carly was manufactured
on a flimsy scaffold of transference, her desire to be seen through
that façade of cool grace. And her knowing, her steady wisdom
of experience, warned her that to fester desire for Carly would
only end badly, messily. And then Ariana thought of Jacqui and
her experience at Wellspring and the irony of her identification,
of her projection. It was OK just to let the wanting be known to
the page and to release it there. Wave it goodbye. It was OK.

Thinking of Jacqui and her doctoral project, Ariana was free
to create another poem. She telephoned, and almost instantly
Jacqui picked up.

'Where are you? I wrote you a poem.'

'What? Really? God, I need it right about now.' Jacqui was
in a computer lab on campus, writing as fast as she could. The
deadline for her first draft was approaching. She had extended
the deadline twice already and didn't want to let it slip further.
She was adamant about meeting that deadline, doing whatever it
took to finish, but her creative impulse was growing weak in the
face of her unyielding determination.

'OK. I'm going to send it by email.'

Jacqui heard Ariana typing on her keyboard, happy she was going to send it right away. Instant gratification.

'Done. So, how's it going?' Ariana asked.

'Uh, OK, I guess. Still so much to do. The more I write, the worse it gets. No kidding.'

'Jacqui, I really doubt that. It must seem like an impossible task, though. I hope my poem keeps you going.'

'Oh, it's here!'

'I'll let you go then. Call me later.' Ariana quickly hung up while Jacqui read her poem. Ariana preferred giving a bit of space to let the words linger, plus she had to be at work in twenty minutes. No time left to dally. It had been a full morning already. She grabbed her tattered bag and dashed out the door.

As Ariana made her way to work, Jacqui read.

> *One Owner*
>
> *the pen has no enemies and no friends*
> *that it knows of   it is a see through thunderstone*
> *half the time it doesn't credit what it's said yet*
> *weird harpie-sharp entity*
> *of wise crone and mixed infantry*
>
> *her slim pickings are fullrich*
> *it is a digging stick, it spells survival*
> *you have to hand it to her,*
> *an open ended pen, no dead*
> *lines, lucidity, herself again*

Jacqui had to hand it to Ariana. Time and again, moved by her words, all things became possible. Quite frequently now, Jacqui was considering, the form her research could take. During the second workshop, Jacqui posed the question to the group, 'What do you think this research should be?' She received many creative responses.

Doris began by explaining food as a commodity, but that there were limits to how much of that commodity a person could consume in a day. Since profits associated with the sale of food were limited, it encouraged food manufacturers to find innovative ways to increase profit margins or increase consumption. Dietitians were caught in this complex political and economic web manipulated by forces outside the profession. Doris thought that if Jacqui's research could show how tangled they were in that web, it would help move their profession forward.

Corine wanted the research to play an expansive role. She imagined video vignettes, human sculpture, and imagery. She wondered what would happen if Jacqui asked a group of students just entering dietetics to self-design their curriculum. 'What would you want to learn about? What would you think you need to learn to become a dietitian?' Jacqui wondered how different the curricula would be and what might be the purpose of such diversity. Were there many routes to the same destination?

Pauline asked for research that is, not does. Nancy wanted to include dietetic students' responses to the question, 'How have your experiences shaped you?' as a means for beginning early reflection on dietetic education. Jacqui agreed that this simple act could have significant effects, because emotion is constituted in the intersubjective, in self-reflection (Crawford, Kippax, Onyx & Gualt, 1992). Questions such as the one Nancy offered could create a shift towards the emotional in the dietetics classroom, the critical emotional, feelings borne through the experience of coming to know oneself.

Then, from Angela, the idea that had intrigued Jacqui the most. 'There's a technique that's used in counselling circles. It's called a reflective group. It's made up of about six people observing an interaction taking place between a client and her therapist. After they finish, the observers take centre stage and talk about their experience of witnessing. It can be profoundly shifting. Extending that, having a group of dietitians talking about similar things we are discussing in this workshop amid a group of dietitians who are simply observing the process. Then the witnessing group would share their experiences and possibly themes they heard. You could even script some dialogue to initiate the process.' As she talked, Angela drew two circles, one inside the other, with arrows indicating the movement of people between them. Jacqui considered the transformative potential of such a performance. She knew these *suggestions, possibilities, provocations, hints, and hopes were luring their speech out into the open.* The question remained, how might she textualize such activities for her dissertation?

Chapter Nine – Thirsty Belief

> *Emotion ... is constituted in the intersubjective:*
> *it is constructed in interaction between people and in our*
> *self-reflection. When we reach an understanding of common*
> *social meanings of events, we are able to use this knowledge*
> *to understand others' experience.*

(Crawford, Kippax, Onyx, & Gualt, 1992, p. 9-10)

Week 9: November 2

Meg sat in class and waited for Tess to begin. Her mind wandered to last class and how tense it had been for her to watch Dr Taylor greet a flustered Tess. She supposed that Dani was pleased about her part in orchestrating that tension. The irony was obvious to Meg. Here they were in class talking about the greater political forces exerting pressure on dietitians, and at the same time Tess was living out the experience. Meg wondered if Tess had made a similar rueful connection. At least in watching it play out from the sidelines, Meg was sure to learn even more than Tess had intended, the unspoken curriculum.

Meg had taken classes with Dr Taylor in the past. She knew the vast difference in teaching styles between the two. She preferred Tess's open, unstructured approach to Dr Taylor's lecturing format. Meg appreciated the space that Tess provided and used it to explore and develop her personal interest in the subject. She wondered if it would make a difference if Tess were teaching clinical nutrition or nutrition assessment, courses more associated with a didactic style. It was hard to know. Not that she hadn't done well in those courses, it was just that she was excited to be learning in a more participatory manner. She was grateful for the opportunity to be in Tess's class. She was glad to have had a different experience at least once before she graduated. She was inspired to take risks here and to truly think about what kind of professional she wanted to become.

Tess began, 'Good morning, everyone. Hello.' The chatter subsided just slightly. 'I just wanted to let you know I've placed your questions and answers from last week on Blackboard. I really enjoyed reading your responses to the questions. Thank you for the time you put into that. For those of you planning to write the final exam instead of a term paper, you will definitely want to take a look at the information on Blackboard. I will be choosing at least one or two questions from that bunch. And for those choosing a final paper, you may also want to take a closer look at that information for topic ideas. I would think two or three of those concepts could be woven together quite nicely for a paper. We could talk about that more on an individual basis. E-mail me anytime.'

Just as Tess finished her introductory remarks, Dani walked in. She appeared not at all apologetic. Tess looked over at her and said hello, but Dani did not respond. Dani's behaviour raised nervous feelings in Meg. Given what she knew, it was like Dani was trying to make a statement to Tess. 'I will come and go as I please. At least that much I can control.' Control. Meg wondered how much of this was about control. Probably a lot.

Tess watched Dani take her place in the back, and the disturbance it created when chairs and bags were moved to allow her to pass. Tess noticed her slight irritation with Dani and tried to remember that both of them were struggling with power and regulation. In that respect, they had much in common. What was going on for her? Tess imagined having Dani's inner critic, her double, perform in character. The vision of such a performance immediately evoked a tenderness in Tess for Dani. It was hard to want things a certain way, your way.

Tess took up her ideas for the day's class. 'Alright. Trust. Let's talk about trust, shall we? First, what did you think and feel after reading Jacqui's paper?'

Meg had been looking forward to talking about this paper. She raised her hand.

Tess did not need to see Meg's hand to know she would have

something to contribute. As if by instinct now, a familiar pattern, 'Yes, Meg, please go ahead.'

'Um, yeah, I have a couple questions about this one. Like, why the poem, why all the psychoanalysis stuff? If we want to do nutrition counselling, how are we supposed to know this stuff? And, what about all the dietitians out there doing nutrition counselling who don't have a clue about psychology?'

'It seems the author is trying to do too much with this piece and it ends up sounding really self-righteous, angry even. There's a lot there.'

'What's Third Space?'

'Why shouldn't clients trust dietitians? I don't get that.'

'I had no idea that Dietitians of Canada accepts funding from pharmaceutical companies. That's pretty insane.'

Tess was not surprised by how the students were responding to the trust article. She remembered when Jacqui showed it to her the first time, and her feedback at the time was to take up one or two strands and elaborate on those. What ended up getting published was pretty close to what Jacqui had shown her in early drafts. It was an ambitious undertaking. So, where to begin?

'OK, I really like your questions – and, yes, the article raises many different issues, illustrated through the use of poetry, virtue theory, philosophy, and ethics. Let's start with ethics. This issue has come up before. The issue with Xenical. Why is it ...'

Dani interrupted Tess, 'Why didn't the author publish this in the DC Journal?'

'Another excellent question, to which I will respond with a question. Why do you think it should have been published there?'

'It obviously deals with an issue related to Canadian dietetic practice. The author names DC as an unethical association. Has Jacqui heard anything from DC about this article?'

'What might you expect her to hear, Dani?'

'Well, I would think DC would be pretty irate to see this in print.'

'So, why would they agree to print it in their journal?'

Dani shrugged.

'The interesting thing is that Jacqui did send this paper to the DC Journal, and the editor refused to send it out for anonymous review. So, there is some controversy here. Despite the editor's efforts to prevent this article from entering academic discourse, you can see that those efforts were foiled.'

To share inside information with the students had created a heightened interest in the article. Tess's description of the publication process had the article looking like it were some kind of rebellious older cousin of all the other published pieces the students had ever read. Tess noticed the students' attention, their rapt silence. She continued. 'Does everyone understand what Jacqui is trying to convey with the accusation of conflict of interest?'

There was no response, so she attempted to bring the strand more clearly into view for the students. She picked up a piece of chalk. 'Jacqui takes up the issue most deliberately starting on page 65, section 6. Could someone please read me her definition of conflict of interest? Let's start there.'

Tess turned to the board, chalk in hand, arm raised, poised to write.

'Yep, OK, "A person is in a conflict of interest situation if she is in a relationship with another in which she has a moral obligation to exercise judgment in that other's service and, at the same time, she has an interest tending to interfere with the proper exercise of judgment in that relationship." That's from Davis, 1982.'

As Meg read, Tess quickly drew two female figures and a very large dollar sign. She labelled each of the symbols and then

Roche

Dietitian   Client

turned to face the class as Meg finished the quote.

'The case for conflict of interest starts with the professional, the dietitian, and I will deliberately use the female pronoun because most dietitians are women. She is morally obligated to exercise professional judgement in the service of her client. Full stop. Now, the labels are problematic. *Service. Client.* These words arise out of a capitalist ideology that doesn't necessarily work for everyone, yet they are there. We'll rely on them for now, acknowledging that the discourse is questionable. Back to our client-dietitian pair. A conflict arises when the dietitian becomes associated with Roche. She is associated with Roche in two different ways. One is through her national association's receipt of sponsorship funding from that drug company. Dietitians of Canada's operating budget is supplemented by funds from Roche. The second is that, through the use of a 1-800 number, physicians prescribing Xenical can contact consulting dietitians to work with their patients who are taking that drug. Now, the dietitian has an interest in receiving those referrals as a potential source of income. One thing you might not be aware of is the ethics of size acceptance. We should really go through that together. The short version is that less and less scientific research really supports the focus on weight loss as a means to health. So, to further complicate matters, dietitians are supporting, by third-party association, the use of drugs for weight loss. Yet, as we discussed several weeks ago – remember Amy's story? – the scientific research reveals that taking Xenical is wrought with physical and psychological dangers. I ask you, can the dietitian properly exercise her professional judgment in the service of that client?'

Silence.

Tess waited, looking around the room, wondering what the students were thinking. One responded.

'I don't think I really get it. So, the dietitian gets a referral to see a patient, … client, whatever, who is taking Xenical. Isn't that a good thing? Isn't it good that the client is being helped by a dietitian and not someone else less knowledgeable?'

'Excellent question. I don't think the problem is with the work that the dietitian does with the client, unless that relationship is influenced somehow by another, potentially conflictual relationship. Is the dietitian grateful for the referral? Yes, of course she is. Does the referral come as an act of disinterested generosity on behalf of Roche or the referring physician? Of course it doesn't. What does Rawlins say on page 66? "No drug company gives away its shareholders' money in an act of disinterested generosity."'

'But Roche and the referring physician don't give the dietitian money. The money comes from the client. What's the big deal?'

'In one way you are right. The client pays for dietitian services. But don't forget that DC receives revenue from Roche towards its operating budget. And we should also acknowledge the work done by Roche to seduce the physician into prescribing its drug and the dietitian into going along with it. Let's see, doctors are given paid vacations, trips to conferences, meals, and gifts by drug companies on a regular basis. Dietitians are invited to dinner seminars sponsored by Roche to hear all about the drug's efficacy and safety. If the drug were that helpful, why the extra campaign? Why wouldn't that just come out through randomized control trials? If dietitians reviewed the literature, like we are taught to do, I agree with Jacqui that we would not be able to support the use of Xenical. Therein lies the second dimension of conflict.'

'Sounds like a conspiracy!'

The students laughed, and Tess did too. She realized that she might be sounding like a conspiracy theorist. Better pull back just a little while the mood was light.

'Ultimately, our good work in society is for naught if we can't be trusted. How does accepting referrals and dinners from a pharmaceutical company instil trust in the dietitian?'

'I think it's pretty brutal that dietitians are associated with drug companies and with Monsanto and Proctor and Gamble and all of them. Aren't we trying to promote healthy eating? It just doesn't make sense to me at all.' Meg was aware of the larger picture. Her comments added credence to Tess's rant. 'It's really all about money. The money is coming between the dietitian and her client,' she said, motioning back to Tess's drawing.

'Yes, it most certainly is, Meg. And, here we are back to capitalism. Can anyone tell me what Jacqui suggests as a solution to this dilemma?'

A young woman who sat beside Meg responded, 'Non-commercial funding?'

'What about increasing the members' fees or providing fewer services?' added Marci, the quiet student from Tess's small group two weeks ago.

Tess had often wondered the exact same thing, 'That seems like a really common sense idea. I have word that member fees are being increased, or at least there will be a vote put to the members about an increase, so it will be interesting to see what happens with that. Usually votes and discussions happen at the annual general meeting, which is held at the annual conference. Not until the end of May I think. Has anyone ever been to the DC conference?'

No one had.

'Does anyone belong to the DC student network?'

Five students raised their hands.

'Who is a student member of DC currently?'

Tess saw that about half the class were student members of DC.

'OK. In the last 30 minutes of class time, I have a letter-to-the-editor writing activity for you to begin. Each of you will write a brief letter, a response regarding the information that Jacqui has presented in her article. Each of you will address your letter to the editor of the journal that published Jacqui's article, 'Agricultural and Environmental Ethics.' Typically, such a letter would address concerns with the article under consideration. Pick one concern you have with the article and focus on that. I expect you to eventually send your letters, but at the very least this will satisfy reader response four.'

Dani raised her hand, 'Are you going to share these with Jacqui?'

Tess thought for a moment before she replied. 'Would you like to share your letter with Jacqui?'

'Uh, I think it would be interesting to get her response, yeah.' Dani answered with the end of her pencil in the corner of her mouth. Tess sensed that Dani was truly interested in getting Jacqui's side of the argument.

Tess paused, thinking of what might be accomplished by sharing each students' writing as part of the class activities. 'Hmmm. What about this? If you would like to share your letter with Jacqui, that would be fine, but you are not expected to do so for the purposes of this activity. It's up to you. Any other questions? …No? OK. You can decide what you feel is most important to address, what concerns you would like to share, to bring to the editor's attention. You might also want to write your letter as a way to acknowledge something that you agree with in the article or to raise another question. It's like asking, "I agree that this is important, but have you considered this, which is equally as important?"'

Sammi, always the intrepid student asked, 'Where do we get the contact information for the editor?'

'Go to the journal website and they should have guidelines for letters to the editor that you will want to review before handing in your final copy to me next week. Reviewing those guidelines could make your task just a little easier by giving you a format to follow.'

Sammi again, 'How long does it have to be?'

'Right. I'm thinking about 300 hundred words, max. No more than a page, page and a half. Just focus on one thing you want to say. Remember, I expect you to actually send your letter. It will count as another reader response, and I expect you to write about the process in your final assignment. Because the letter counts as a reader response, please print me a copy for next week. If there are no more questions, why don't you spend the last twenty minutes getting started? I hope that some of you will share your letters with us at the beginning of next class. I would really enjoy that.'

Tess finished her description of the writing activity and hoped, as usual, that it was clear enough.

❧

'I'm tired of doing laundry, Jacq.'

The apartment was quiet now that Evyn was sleeping. Jacqui had poured two glasses of their favourite Shiraz and handed Kelly hers as she came down the stairs from Evyn's room. This was a special time for the two of them, an important time to reconnect after being apart all day. Jacqui was aware of the sacrifices Kelly was making so she could finish her doctorate. It had been only a few months since Kelly finished her own degree, an undergraduate in human geography and First Nations studies. They had decided together that Kelly wouldn't return to work after her parental leave ended. Instead they were going to try to make it through, financially and emotionally, with Kelly being a full-time, stay-at-home mom while Jacqui continued on with her private practice and prepared her dissertation.

Curling into the corner of the couch, nestled in with Cleo, their once-feral, now overwhelmingly reliant black cat, Jacqui asked, 'Do you regret quitting your job?' Jacqui realized her question didn't really attend to the deep layers of Kelly's multiple subjectivities.

'No, it's not that. I love being with Evyn more than anything else. It's just really tiring. It's draining.'

'Yeah, I understand. I know. You are so amazing and steady to do what you do every day. Evyn is such a lucky girl to have you with her. I wish I could be here, too.' Jacqui found it difficult to leave the house each morning, turning back to see Evyn waving goodbye. So adorable! When did she learn to do that? Jacqui marvelled at the changes in their life. Only a year ago, she was still pregnant, waddling around as big and as awkward as a house, complaining with every step. Now, this toddler was emerging in their presence. It was all completely wondrous to both of them, wondrous and draining.

'Is this what you imagined it would be like?'

Kelly pondered Jacqui's question. 'I'm not sure. I didn't imagine there would be so much laundry or so many dishes! It's endless.'

'If you could choose between having a washer/dryer or a dishwasher, what would you choose?'

Kelly smiled, 'Dream big! Well, I would have to say a dishwasher. That would really free up some time from being in the kitchen.'

'Yeah, I'll say. What is it the parenting books say – when your baby sleeps, that's time for you, downtime. Right! So if you're not doing dishes then, when will they get done?'

Kelly got to the heart of her concern. 'I'm really worried that you're going to start finding me quite dull. What's so exciting about your partner whose main job in life is washing dishes, doing laundry, cleaning bathrooms, and vacuuming? There are so many other people in your life. People you can have stimulating conversations with, like Ariana or Tess. I'm becoming my worst nightmare. Why did I even bother getting a degree if I can't even carry on a halfway intellectual conversation with you?'

Jacqui's brow furrowed. She immediately realized that her going off to write was a luxury and was viewed by society as more meaningful, more visible than the intensely difficult yet abundantly more important work of mothering. This was an interesting quandary they found themselves in, two mothers, one having birthed Evyn being out of the home more than the other. Both mothers being pulled to be home, to be full and equal partners in the parenting of their child. Both of them having so much to offer that baby girl and both of them having so much to learn from her, too.

Jacqui reached for Kelly's hand. 'Oh, sweetheart! You are incredible; intelligent, funny, loving. You bring our family stability and fill us with love everyday. I know that you will continue on with your education at some point in the future. We appreciate you so much!'

Jacqui couldn't begin to overstate her deep love for Kelly and their daughter. She realized that for both of them to have parental and academic aspirations was at times daunting, but their mutual love and respect sustained them through the difficult periods. Jacqui made it through because Kelly was there to share the challenges. They did it together. The givenness of their family, the unconditional stability afforded by Kelly and her unwavering loyalty, was all Jacqui could have asked for in her life. It was Jacqui's deep intention to reassure Kelly of her gifts, and still it didn't seem enough.

ằ·

November 7

Dear Ms Gingras,

I'm writing in response to your article, 'Evoking trust in the nutrition counsellor: why should we be trusted?' I wondered why the article wasn't published in the *DC Journal*, but my instructor told me that they didn't like it very much. I guess I can understand why. It's pretty severe. Has DC said anything to you about the article being published in the other journal?

My main question is more about your work with eating disorders. Do you think many dietitians have eating disorders? Is that why they become dietitians, to try to figure out food and what to eat? What happens when a dietitian who has an eating disorder tries to advise someone else with an eating disorder? I've been thinking about this for a while now. What would you advise someone who wants to help people recover, but who is really in the middle of his or her own problems with food? Is it really possible to recover from an eating disorder? I read that the success rate is pretty low. I think it would also be harder for dietitians to admit they had a problem since they are supposed to know better. I imagine there is a lot of secrecy about all of it. What do you think? Who can a dietitian trust to give her help with this? How is it possible, as you quote, 'to forgive and ... be forgiven' for poor choices with food? I don't really understand the part you quoted in section five about 'standing in the spaces.' What happens when we give up control? Could you explain that further and what is meant by 'Third Space?' I don't really get that concept.

I would like to write my final paper on this topic, so if you have any time to respond in the next couple of days, that would be great.

Sincerely,
Dani Sutherland

༄

November 2

Dear Judith,

In *Undoing Gender* (Butler, 2004), you say *The Hegelian tradition links desire with recognition, claiming that desire is always a desire for recognition and that it is only through the experience of recognition that any of us becomes constituted as socially viable beings (p. 2).* Yes, I agree that view has its allure and its truth but it also misses a couple of important points since the terms by which we are recognized as human are socially articulated and changeable. And then you add, and here is where it becomes complex for me: *But if the schemes of recognition that are available to us are those that 'undo' the person by conferring recognition or 'undo' the person by withholding recognition, then recognition becomes a site of power by which the human is differentially produced* (Butler, 2004, p. 2). OK. I follow you on each of these accounts. And, given my persisting fixation, I invoke a turn, and, following an impulse of integrity, I ask you, what might these claims mean if read through the experience of being dietitian? Who qualifies as recognizable and who does not? What are the implications? And, what might this mean for feminist phenomenology, the methodological movement of my choosing?

First, I thank you for giving me the permission to perplex the common sense of dietetic identity. It took me a great deal of time to render this research as a feminist phenomenology. It seemed like I was standing in a field of traditions of method and theory, a wildly undulating kaleidoscope of colour in the wind like wildflowers, wild methods and theory, each eye-catching and determinate. It was for me to decide among these movements, these swaying flowers. (How did they get there in that field? How did I?) In the end, I was bound to *distinguish among their norms and conventions that permit people [me] to breathe, to desire, to love, and to live, and those norms and conventions that restrict or eviscerate the conditions of life itself* (Butler, 2004, p. 8). This choosing between *differences in position and desire* – not picking the flowers mind you, just me harboured in their essence – *set the limits to universalizability as an ethical reflex* (p. 8). It is true, it is right for me, it says much of who I am when I agree that this critique must be situated within the context of lives as they are lived and must be guided by the question of what maximizes the possibilities for a liveable life, what minimizes the possibility of an unbearable life or, indeed, social or literal death (Butler, 2004, p. 8). And what's also important in this ethical reflex, as you call it, is that it be right and true for those invited to join with me into the process we call research. This aspect is especially important to me. I believe I have some sense of accomplishment from engaging in research in this way and the proof of this accomplishment is difficult to capture with this alphabet. The proof is in the stories we shared and the feelings we felt. But what of the stories that were not shared? I have some small doubts about this because I could only trust my intuition to sense the withholding that might have gone on, and my senses suggest that this did happen from time to time. The silence has so many different meanings and, I dare say, the silence says so much. hooks says 'Our silence shields us from uncertainty' (hooks, 2000, p. xxvi). This much might be true. Needless to say, it is a complicated silence, and to explore the silence, just as to explore gender, we are, quite inadvertently, caught up in ontological thickets and epistemological quandaries (Butler, 2004, p. 16). I'm pleased to discover that poetry is alive in your discourse. What an unrivalled sense of relief that is for me!

On the topic of gender – it is a fair topic, yes, for almost all dietitians are women ... are female, are ...? I find myself in thickets
and quandaries. *The 'I' who ought to be bearing its gender is undone by being a gender, that gender is always coming from a source
that is elsewhere and directed towards something that is beyond me,
constituted in a sociality I do not fully author* (Butler, 2004, p. 16).
Should I not make those claims? Does my speech cease towards
transformation? Does my feminist tongue become boneless, politically naïve? No. That can't be it. *It only means that when one makes
those claims, one makes them for much more than oneself* (Butler,
2004, p. 16).

Judith, I apologize for the length of this correspondence. It seems
that when I ventured away from *The Psychic Life of Power* towards
poetry, Okri and Rukeyser, I was then able to be with your words in a
more spacious, intelligible, and composed manner, and it has opened
me to your own current writings, which I notice have changed, too.
What's more, the letters, this alphabet I had been relying on to craft
these meanings, became unwieldy, although my spirit has not.

In-spire,
Jacqui

৯

It was Sunday afternoon. Jacqui was sitting in the back corner
of the teashop, indulging in a *People* magazine while she waited
for Tess. They rarely found the time to meet on weekends, but
because they hadn't met for what seemed like months, this time
seemed necessary. Weekends were usually family times, but both
Jacqui and Tess understood that family time was enhanced when
parents' lives were balanced. Being balanced, feeling supported
was what this tea date was all about.

The rain outside ordained the teashop a tranquil sanctuary – a
humid refuge of cozy armchairs, steaming cups of tea, heavenly
pastries, the seduction of light jazz. Jacqui barely took in any of
it while reading *People*. It was a weakness for her – the maga-

zine consumed her entirely. She was deeply lost to arcane pop culture when Tess finally approached, startling Jacqui out of her *People*-induced trance. Jacqui quickly rolled up the magazine and stuffed it between her leg and the side of the chair.

'I saw that,' teased Tess.

'What?' Jacqui's denial was fruitless. 'Oh, this? Uh, I have no idea where it came from.'

'I guess you can be forgiven this time. I don't suppose you do much reading for enjoyment these days.' Tess bent to hug and kiss her friend.

'No, I don't. Poor me.' Jacqui loved Tess's bergamot essence, barely perceptible, but there when she leaned in close. The smell tingled Jacqui's senses.

Tess twisted out of her purple rain jacket and hung it dripping wet on a coat rack nearby. She casually ran her fingers through her wild spray of graying curls. Tess was captivating yet completely unaware of the effect she could have. Jacqui noticed a male customer watching Tess, attempting to be discreet behind his newspaper. She struck a compelling figure, even in her Levis and simple t-shirt. It was her height and her energy and her fluidity. If you were lucky enough to face her directly, her emerald green eyes then compelled even further. And, yet, Tess was oblivious to it all, preferring to be inconspicuous, content in her life.

'Have you ordered?' Tess asked, reaching for a tea menu. 'I'm feeling like I want to try something a little different today.'

'Want to try matcha?'

'Hmmm, what's matcha?' Tess lowered her menu.

'It's a green tea, but instead of steeping the leaves, you drink them. They grind the leaves into a fine powder and make the tea with the powder. Lots of antioxidants.'

'Well, you know how much I love my antioxidants! I'll try a cup of the matcha.'

Jacqui smiled, stood, and made her way to the counter to place their order.

Tess looked around the teashop and noticed her surroundings

for the first time. They had been meeting here for tea for several months, since before she had started teaching. Tess was aware of the tradition they were creating, of the predictability of space. It was important for her to have this time, especially because the rest of her world was spinning madly out of control.

Tess embraced the meditative ambience of the teashop, and focused on her breath. Her eyes closed, and she became aware of the tightness in her neck and shoulders. She breathed deeply into those spaces, the interstices of her cells, ripe with memory of conflict, loss, and regret. She imaged her muscles to release, beckoned nerves to untangle, and teased lungs to engorge with oxygen. Lately, she had been practising meditation in every moment she had. She was being reminded by the people and events of her life to return to what mattered. To be mindful. Tess used to meditate every day and then she stopped, but she couldn't remember why. Last week, while quickly eating her tuna sandwich in the community health lunchroom, her dietitian colleague Doris told her of her recent diagnosis of breast cancer. Tess remembered hearing the news and feeling like she had been kicked hard in the stomach. She couldn't breath. She leaned over and held Doris, a woman she had worked with for over ten years and whom she hadn't ever touched before. Tess wasn't sure who had offered the support and who received it. Tess realized that, reliving the memory of Doris and her breast cancer, she had become distracted from her breath. She gently reminded herself to return to a still point when she heard the sturdy ceramic tea bowls being placed on the low, mahogany table in front of her. Tess's eyes opened to matcha.

'Oh, wow, what an interesting shade of green.' Tess leaned forward and with both hands gingerly picked up her bowl of matcha and took a tentative sip.

'Well?' Jacqui's matcha was frothier, but just as peculiarly green.

'Mmmm. It's like a thick green tea. I think I like it. What about the latté?' Tess took another sip, less cautious this time.

'Uh, mine's kinda gritty. It feels like my teeth are coated with sand.'

'Like swamp water! Maybe there's a frog in there somewhere?'

'Oh, my God, Tess. That's just great. Lovely! Clearly not the matcha tea ceremony of traditionalists!'

'No way!' Both Tess and Jacqui laughed, appreciative of the time they had to joke about their tea.

Jacqui looked over her bowl of iridescent green foam and asked, 'So, how is the class going? It's been so long. I can't believe it's just over a week before I come to speak about my research.'

'I know. The term is flying by, as I thought it might. I feel a little like I'm caught in the eye of a cyclone, though. There is drama.'

'Oh, I love drama. What could it be?'

'Well, without disclosing names – one of the students has complained to Alice about my teaching style. Don't even ask me who it is because I won't tell you.'

'A hint?'

'No hints, no clues. Plus, I don't want it to influence your interactions with the students when you join us on the 16th. I completely know where this young woman is coming from. I recognize so much of my younger self in her. That's not the real challenge for me. I can create a space for dissention. It's that Alice dropped in on one of my classes a couple weeks ago. Talk about awkward – and for the first time, I was running late. God, it was miserable.'

Jacqui watched and listened to Tess for signs of how she was doing with the pressure of the academy bearing down on her. She appeared to be holding up well, at least from the outside. 'Did she say anything to you about it afterwards?'

'No, just asked if the student had talked to me directly, which she just had. Alice is so busy, she really doesn't want to get caught up in it. She seems relatively convinced things are as they should be. Nothing much else was said.'

'Yeah, but what wasn't said? What was left unsaid?' Jacqui was feeling riled, protective of her friend.

'I know. I get the impression that I won't be asked back if I create much more turmoil for Alice and her students.'

Jacqui was a little surprised that Tess was expecting to be asked back. 'Were you expecting to teach that class again? I thought Alice was just going on a four-month research leave.'

'Yes, that's right. But when we first met last April to discuss the possibility of my teaching this term, she also mentioned that she was hoping to develop other courses and may need someone to teach NUTR 430 in the upcoming years. So, she didn't make any promises, but I would love to be a part of something longer term.'

Jacqui sensed that much of how Tess defined herself was bound up in the curriculum of NUTR 430. Not to be invited to participate in future offerings might be interpreted as her self not being valued as worthy. Always a risky situation for sessionals in the academy: no power to make decisions, a cog in the academic production wheel. Dispensable. 'I'm sorry it is becoming so complicated. Both you and the students are under a great deal of stress. Students applying for internships, needing to do well in fourth-year courses. You wanting to be asked back. So much is at stake.' Jacqui didn't really know what else to say. She felt inadequate in the face of power struggles. It wouldn't help to get angry or philosophical. Most of the time, it didn't help at all.

'I know. There isn't much to say. I was just thinking, though, before the matcha came, about the extreme fragility of life. Do you remember Doris at Central Downtown Health?' Jacqui nodded. 'She was just diagnosed with metastatic breast cancer.'

'Oh, no! That's terrible.'

'I know. She just told me this week. I don't really know what she was doing at work, but I imagine she feels an obligation to her home-care clients. She plans to do some chemo, but if it gets to be too much, she will stop. It's tragic.'

'Makes you think, doesn't it?'

'Well, that's just it. While we were talking about her diagnosis,

Doris told me about a time in her life that she called "The Living Death." She realized that she just was not happy doing what she was doing – that is, working in clinical nutrition – so she made some changes. And now she's so grateful to have done it. I think she was trying to tell me to slow down, appreciate my family, and do something that I love. At least that's what I hear myself thinking more and more these days.'

'So what would you change in your life?'

'Oh, that's easy. I would work less and spend more time with Zoë. Maybe take her to Italy.'

Jacqui noticed that Tess didn't mention Michael. 'And what if you don't? What if you don't make that change?'

'I don't know, Jacq.' Tess was silent for a moment. She peered into her bowl of matcha like she would find her answer there, swimming among the green depths. 'When Doris was telling me about her "Living Death," there was a large part of me that wanted to say, "Yeah, me too!" but I was afraid. Afraid to admit it. I've always known myself to be so clear and together. Lately, I've been a madwoman. I mean, just look at how my inner Bitch is behaving!'

Both women laughed at the memory of Tess's performance. It was compelling theatre, to say the least, but it was also Tess's life. Her real life. Maybe their laughter was to cover the anguish of it, not only for Tess, but also for her friends and colleagues who, it seemed, were struggling with major life issues, too.

'Why are we so invested in dietetics? I mean, forget the money. I hear more and more about the despair, the "Living Deaths" we are performing and I just don't understand why a group of highly intelligent, creative women are feeling stuck in their lives. What's going on?' Tess's eyes had a faraway look. She was truly at a loss to answer her own question.

Jacqui waded in, pretending she had something to say about the topic. 'You know, with my research, I'm becoming more and more convinced that we possess a strong desire for recognition, and, not finding that, not feeling we are being seen, we fall into grief and eventually melancholia. That might be what Doris is calling her "Living Death." Remember when Carly got into the psychoanalysis about it all as a means for supporting Gabi? That's what it's about for us, I think.'

Tess was looking as confused now as she had felt in their supervision group. 'Who do we want to get that recognition from?'

'Maybe we enter the profession thinking we can make a difference, a real difference in the lives of others. That is a genuine reason many of us get into this work. But it's offset by the other reasons we get into dietetics, to make money, to be secure, to be in the health industry. Those are cultural symbols of recognition, but, on their own, they can never be enough to give our life meaning. We are experiencing an existential crisis.'

Tess considered this as a possibility through the lens of her own experience. 'Maybe. Existential crisis. Hmmm. Maybe.'

'What would it mean if your students went through an existential crisis in their class with you instead of five, ten, fifteen years into their career?'

'Whoa! That's not going to go over well. Things are already in chaos, and you want to introduce an existential crisis? My friend, Jacqui, the saboteur!' Tess was shaking her head, while her green eyes danced and her lips curled in friendly scorn.

'No! OK, let me reframe that. Hold on! What if those students were told the truth about their work as dietitians?'

'What do you mean "the truth"? That dietetics is political and emotional?'

'Yes. Because it *is* political and emotional, and not knowing that beforehand is kind of a major ruse that we're setting up for those students. It's like, "Here's the knowledge you need to go and be a dietitian. That's all you need. Go forth and prosper." Well, you and I both know that's not all they need. That's why you are teaching the course in this way. It's an act of hopefulness in the face of the "living death." And, I admire you immensely for it.'

'Ah, well, thanks Jacq. It's hard, but you're right, it is important to me to make these attempts, feeble and misunderstood as they might be.'

A moment of quiet befell their conversation. Both women thought about their collective contributions to the profession in which they found themselves, and how those contributions figured in the full lives they had composed in deliberate and accidental ways. Both were at the same time grateful and unfulfilled, sated and hungry. Both were compelled by *the beauty of thirsty belief,* and both would not give up. The desire for recognition summoned them forth, a deep longing, perpetual and unanticipated, a thirst to be seen for who they already were.

Chapter Ten – Surrender Lament

What we need is lament and mourning and grieving
for what we have done in the name
of our own ascendancies and aspirations.

(Jardine, 1998, p. 143)

Week 10: November 9

There seemed to be a widening abyss between Meg and Dani. Meg thought it started the day they talked about Dani's complaints about the course. Despite Dani's complaints, Meg didn't feel much sympathy for her. It was hard for Meg to feel compassion for someone with such an overpowering sense of entitlement and privilege. The gap between them had widened when Dr Taylor had sat in on their class a couple weeks earlier. Meg sensed that this visit from Dr Taylor provided Dani a great deal of satisfaction. Meg thought that response was completely inappropriate, maybe because she knew why Dr Taylor was there. It all just seemed really inauthentic. One thing Meg knew for sure, the chasm between them was of no consequence to Dani. Meg was sure Dani didn't even care what she thought.

Tess's voice broke in on Meg's thoughts. 'Good morning. I'm looking forward to reading your letters. Please pile them here, those who haven't already done so.' Tess got right to the task. It was even a little before 9:00 am. Dani hadn't yet arrived.

As the students slowly filed up to her table, Tess continued, 'Today we are going to talk about Gussow's article and then do something that isn't commonly done, and that is to revisit a paper we've already talked about. Consider it an experiment.' Tess instantly regretted suggesting anything she did was experimental. She felt great risk in being experimental, alternative, unprepared, uncertain. 'Well, not really an experiment. More like time to reflect on what we've learned so far, coming round to the beginning.' Tess also believed this was an hermeneutic process, but she refused to say it out loud for fear of being judged as obscure. Clearly Tess was performing 'woman under (self) surveillance.'

Meg noticed Tess's reversal on the use of 'experiment.' She wondered how much this thing with Dani and Dr Taylor had shaken her resolve. Something innocent in Meg twisted when she saw Tess, a moral person, being troubled and disrupted by people like Dani and Dr Taylor. Is this what happens when you believe in something non-conventional? Meg knew the reality of her own experience, but still wanted to hang on to her idealism. She wished her reality were different.

'I would like to start with Gussow. Can anyone guess why I included this little article in the syllabus?' Tess was all business.

No one responded. Most were still arranging their notebooks and pens. A couple of students were still milling around Tess's table with their reader-response papers. Tess didn't wait but answered her own question.

'Even though this class isn't about sustainability or environmental education, which are worthy topics on their own, it is about ethics and professionalism. What Gussow shares in coming back twelve years later to her promotion of sustainability is how people responded to her original piece and what effect that has on her current thinking and practice.'

Tess was in full lecture mode this morning. She placed a transparency on the overhead, although its content was temporarily hidden beneath a piece of paper. Still, some students began to take notes, which caused others to take notes as well, a chain reaction.

'Gussow's paper begins with a history of her promotion of sustainability. It seems that not everyone was in favour of her promotion of such a concept. How anyone can be against sustainability is beyond me to comprehend, but sometimes the most commonsensical ideas are not widely embraced. This is where Martinez, Gussow, and Gingras intersect, and you will need to pay close attention here.'

Just as Tess finished, Dani made her entrance. Although everyone initially turned to watch her, their attention quickly returned to Tess. They were somewhat nonplussed by such an unusual opening for one of her classes, and sat poised to copy whatever information the transparency held. Their pens and their attention were poised as Tess snaked back the paper from her transparency, revealing the words *resistance, power,* and *conflict.* Tess started making the connections between the three words before Dani actually sat down.

'When members of an organization... let's just say when a dietetics organization presents ideas that it believes to be for the betterment of that organization and of society, there is often resistance. The resistance is often cloaked by power. The source of the power is only that which individuals have given the organization. Ironically, the resistance creates conflict between individual and organizational values and goals. Notice the phrase in Gussow's article, "willing to subvert their professionality in order to promote their social cause" (Gussow, 1999). Can one not be professional and still promote a social cause? Do no professionals promote social causes? What does it mean to be a professional? Another quotation from Gussow, and one that speaks to all of what we're working through in this course, is "How is it that we tend to accept as objective assertion that the *status quo* is just fine and denounce as subjective or biased statements that question the way things are?" Who here has an answer to that question?'

Tess was shifting into an evangelical delivery. Again, she didn't wait for an answer. Her next transparency was placed for viewing. Three more words: *fear, subjectivity, ethics.*

'In my experience, we accept the status quo out of fear. We fear uncertainty, we fear ambiguity, we fear we might have been mistaken, we fear our own vulnerability. We could build a case here for how power resists subjectivity, which is to say power resists change even if it is morally derived, ethically justified.'

When Tess stopped speaking, she noticed the room was unusually silent, like when Alice had visited. Today, it suited her just fine. She referenced her notes and replaced the previous transparency with another: *local, global, capitalism.*

'On page 196 of Gussow's article, she draws in the concept of capitalism and free trade when she says, "The sustainability of the food system is also threatened by the normal working of free trade." As she describes how the foods that we eat originate from beyond our borders, our thoughts should turn to the processes, the human effort required to complete the production of that food. Our thoughts should become global thoughts. We might become aware of such practices on a global scale, getting a clearer sense of the impact of our local choices, literally how our choices push forcefully against people in other parts of the world. We have already talked about capitalism's relationship with dietetic practice and professionalism when we discussed Austin's article, and here we have yet another example.'

Tess had barely taken a breath, and she showed no signs of returning to the open, dialogic style the students had grown accustomed to from earlier classes. Next overhead: *responsibility, professionalism, abandonment of practical wisdom.*

'My favourite part of Gussow's article comes on page 199. "I hold nutrition educators at least partially responsible for the abandonment of food preparation; we have sought to avoid being associated with 'home economics,' bought into the convenience food trend, and have not accepted it as our responsibility to teach the joys of quick and easy food preparation from scratch, using produce that is in season at various times of the year." Can we acknowledge that responsibility for abandoning home economics? I would speculate that one's intense disparagement of sustainability is a creative way around accepting responsibility. I say creative; some might say devious or unprofessional.'

Tess pursued the 'abandoning of the home economics thread.' 'How many of you know that dietetics emerged from home economics over a hundred years ago?'

Not one student put up there hand. Tess looked at Dani. Dani stared back at her, but did not indicate she knew this to be true.

Dani still had not written any notes or made any attempt to do so.

Tess's next question: 'How many of you have enjoyed your food prep course?'

Only about ten hands went up, perhaps because students were still busy trying to copy information off the overheads. There was an unnaturally fast pace to the day's class.

'OK. How many people have heard other people complain about their food prep course?'

Almost everyone put up their hands. Tess heard some snickering near the back of the room.

'What are the complaints that people have heard?'

Dani said, brazenly, 'It's a waste of time.'

Meg softened Dani's reply with, 'Lots of students are trying to reinforce this belief that dietitians don't have to be cooks, so they would prefer doing other classes, like science classes or electives rather than food prep.'

Tess responded, 'Well, we can see the impact of not learning food prep when we read Gussow's article. Is it a waste of time to encourage people to eat local foods when they can and help them learn how to prepare such foods? What does a dietitian do?'

Tess let her question hang in the air for a few moments. She gathered her plastic sheets together, turned to the last page of Gussow's article, and offered her final commentary.

'So, what does Gussow suggest we do about all of this twelve years later? She quotes author Susan Witt. "It will take imagination, courage, and a community ready to meet the initial inconveniences of a changing lifestyle if we are to build sustainable economies." Imagination, courage, and readiness. I agree. Now it's your turn. Before we turn our attention back to Travers's piece, I want you to spend seven minutes in a free-writing exercise sharing your response to this question.' Tess placed her final transparency on the overhead. It read, *What kind of education is required to support students in becoming dietitians with imagination and courage, dietitians who are embracing change in themselves and others?*

The students read silently.

Tess said nothing, and some of the students stared at her expectantly. Tess decided that her presence during this writing exercise might be distracting, so she told the students she would be right back and then left the room. As she walked down the hallway, she reflected on the morning's pedagogical overture. She thought about how easy it was just to tell students what she wanted them to know, to pour the information into their brains. Almost a default position, it came back to her so quickly, so instinctively. It was how she was taught, yes, but that was years ago. She doubted Alice would have visited or Dani complained had she delivered the entire course in this style. The realization troubled her considerably. It was not her way to impart knowledge. It was not co-creative. It was not embracing of others' experiences. Sure, once in a while it can be a great way to provide course content, but in this case, how much of it was about punishing the students? How much of this approach was about exerting her own power? Why did she need to exert power over the students? She admitted the applicability of that question. She acknowledged the parallels between her discussion of Gussow's article and her own didactic performance. The acknowledgment made her feel slightly queasy. She entered the women's washroom and looked at her tired reflection in the mirror. Her only thought was, 'Can you acknowledge your own responsibility? Can you?' Tess lowered her eyes, her hands gripped the edge of the counter, her shoulders slumped. She knew that she could not.

When Tess returned to the classroom, the first person she saw was Alice. A flash of guilt and sense of the ridiculous spread through her chest. Why was it that she couldn't manage to actually be in the classroom when Alice decided to drop by? Alice, who was sitting, rose to meet Tess. Tess noticed an odd expression on Alice's face. Her stomach lurched violently.

'Can I talk to you outside, Tess?'

Alice ushered Tess out of the room. Tess didn't notice that Alice was holding Tess's bag and coat. The students sat still and quiet.

They had stopped writing as soon as Alice arrived. They had no idea what was happening.

Alice closed the door behind them, which blocked the students from finding out what was going on. When she turned from the door, Tess asked, 'What's going on?'

Alice would have preferred not to have to been the one to tell Tess. Her voice was low. 'There's been an accident, Tess. The hospital called. Zoë is there right now.'

Tess's hand covered her mouth. 'What? What hospital? Oh, my God! Oh, my God!' Tess couldn't breathe.

'The receptionist has already called you a cab. It's waiting for you outside. Here's your coat and your things. You shouldn't be driving.'

'What happened?' Tess couldn't focus. She wanted to run. Her legs wouldn't move.

'Tess, I don't know. All I know is that she is at the General. You should go.' Alice held Tess's arm and walked her out to the waiting taxi.

Tess repeated over and over, 'Oh, my God.' Her eyes wild and glassy.

Alice helped Tess as she stepped into the cab and ordered the driver to take her to the General as fast as he could. The car left as Alice watched from the sidewalk. 'Let it be OK. Let her be OK.' Grim-faced, she returned to the students and told them something had come up and Tess won't be able to return today. She told them to check their email for instructions about their next class, and with that she left. She didn't want to say anything more personal. It was best if she didn't.

Tess's driver expertly manoeuvred his car through the light traffic to get Tess to the General in record time. Her hand shook as she opened her bag and reached for her purse.

'Ma'am, the fare has been taken care of already,' the driver reassured her.

'Oh, oh. OK. Thanks.' Tess leaped out of the car, her legs now hypermobile, and dashed into the Emergency admitting.

'My daughter was brought in. Where is my daughter?' Tess yelled frantically as she approached the nurses on duty.

One nurse responded, 'Ma'am, slow down. What is your daughter's name?'

'Zoë, Zoë Leung. She was just brought in, for God's sake.' Tess was quickly becoming hysterical.

The nurse didn't bother to check the computer. 'Come with me.'

'What happened? Is she OK? Is my husband with her?'

'Ma'am, you will have to wait to speak to the attending physician. Yes, your husband is here.'

The nurse quickly led Tess through a labyrinth of hallways to Zoë's room. Tess pulled open the door, her heart convulsed with fear at what she might see. On the threshold, she stopped dead in her tracks. There was Zoë. Her eyes were closed. Why were they closed? There was Michael, holding Zoë's hand. He looked up to see her. She searched for answers in his face and could only see strain. Both Zoë and Michael were exceptionally pale.

'Michael. Oh, my God!' Tess tried to move forward, but the room suddenly spun around her terrified body. Tess reached out, but her hand found nothing. She saw the look of astonishment on Michael's face as he took a step towards her and as the nurse behind her said, 'Oh, no!' And then only darkness.

ﻌ

Jacqui sat at her desk, unable to write. It was after lunch, and her energy was lagging. She opened her web browser. Google News. Click. *Indonesia Gives Australian Woman 20-Year Term. Muslims Denounce Koran Abuse. Alberta Child Killer Sentenced to Life. Bomb at Pakistan Mosque Kills 19 People.* Jacqui's response to the news was one of sorrow. And she felt the sorrow and treacherous ache even more deeply after she had a child of her own. It seemed like before Evyn was born she was living mostly on the surface of things. Not letting herself be touched deeply by others' suffering. And now, when she read the news, it was all suffering. All of it. She looked for distraction. Didn't anyone have something good to report? Sports. Click. Something caught her eye. 'Home favourite Ariana Willingdon wins back to back titles.' What? Ariana never mentioned she was in a race last week. Jacqui read that Ariana not only won the women's division, but bested her time of one year ago. She was inspired by this news. Small wonder. Grateful for the shift in her mood, it was the perfect time to reciprocate the gift of Ariana's poem from two weeks ago and honour Ariana's running accomplishment, Jacqui wrote.

Home Favourite

caught up
carried away
your words
deeds
speak me undone
urge, press, lift me
incessant
all the right words
bleed your pen empty
leave me breathless

longing to run
limbs limber of time
unshackled
ready-set-go
laces flamenco
pull curious ones
eager around bends
what's written there?

catch me

no, race me
through hilly text before
my feet leaden in muddy thoughts
dirty pen, scratches, rips half letters
shreds wet vowels
gasp alphabets as air
weep for meaning
write truth in sprints
start at the finish

and you know what I mean
your heart kindly punctuates paragraphs of sorrow
your Okri whispers cool in my throat
urgent little rivulets spelling beauty
in the grime of muscled legs
thorn scratched arms wave me onward
caught up
cartographies of motion
swirl
spin
weave

contest worlds in words
race home sceptical
leave the ground
in your tremulous strides
imagine me this

Jacqui worked on the poem for most of the afternoon, knowing she should write something academic, but not being able to bring herself to the task. By three o'clock, she felt satisfied with the poem, but more than slightly sheepish for not spending more time on other writing projects. She felt burdened knowing that Kelly was home with Evyn, doing the hard, exhausting work of mothering, while Jacqui was free to come and go as she pleased. This sacrifice was not lost on Jacqui. She began another poem.

Astonished

I stand beside you
Midst the swirl of our life
We spin wildly together
And our little girl smiles
To watch us inseparable.

Hug, hug, hug! Oh, hug!
Mommies hug!

We make plans
Big dreams
We work hard
Not afraid to labour
Aching backs, bruises

The hard work that love demands
And we do it, willingly. Happily.

Apple-red choices
Picked from trees of dreams
Look what you've done!
Pride swells
Joy full of love

Through the toil of learning
The deep dirt of heartache
Look what you've done!
I'm amazed by you.
We stand at the edge of all that is good
I look over
My partner
My eyes light
My heart skips
I'm amazed by you.

Hear me this time.

We jump from that edge
Hand gripping hand
And all I can hear is your heart
singing in flight.

Jacqui, though not quite finished, was vaguely satisfied. She shut down her computer, gathered her things, and dashed off to catch the bus. As she stepped outside, the wind and the rain defied her with their intensity. Jacqui forced herself forward, eager to be home with Kelly and Evyn, still unaware that her very good friend Tess was at the hospital, conscious again, still in a fog of terror, and settled in for a long vigil at the bedside of her darling daughter, Zoë. It would be a very long night for both of them.

≥▲

As Jacqui left the campus, not a few buildings away Alice picked up her ringing phone. It was Michael, Tess's partner.

'Hello, is this Dr Taylor?'

'Yes, this is Alice.'

'Uh, hello. This is Michael Leung, Tess's husband. I'm just phoning to thank you for getting Tess to the hospital today. I'm very sorry you had to disrupt the class.'

'Oh, for goodness sake, Michael. Don't worry about the class. Please tell Tess not to worry about anything at all.' Alice paused and wondered if it would be too personal to ask Michael for more information, but did anyway. 'What are the doctors saying?'

'The doctors are cautious. We want to believe the best, but Zoë is still unconscious.'

'I see.' Alice thought she was treading too deeply in personal matters. She wanted to cut their conversation short. She was fearful of the truth. 'Michael, please give my very best to Tess. Tell her that I will be happy to step in with her class. Tell her not to worry about one single thing.'

'Thanks, Alice. I will tell her. Good-bye.'

Alice hung up and shuddered at the memory of telling Tess the news that her daughter had been hurt. The memory of the wave of panic across Tess's face shook Alice. What could she do? She was Tess's employer, not her friend. She thought that she should take over the class for Tess. Of course, now was not good timing, with a grant proposal due in three days and two papers waiting for her to revise and resubmit, but these were unusually desperate circumstances and it seemed the least she could offer.

෪

Jacqui stepped off the bus and looked towards home. She could see Kelly and Evyn waiting for her on their front doorstep. She waved, and Kelly waved back. Jacqui crossed the street and came up the sidewalk to their front door. When Evyn noticed her, her entire face smiled, and they both shrieked with joy.

'Hello, baby girl! Heeelllllloooo!' Jacqui ran the last few steps and swept Evyn out of Kelly's arms and spun her around. Even as the rain fell down on them, they both laughed and were happy. Jacqui pulled Evyn in close to her and nuzzled her neck, kissing her over and over, breathing her in. Kelly stood under cover.

'You have a phone message, darling.'

'Oh, really.' Jacqui didn't want to be disturbed from her welcome-home ritual.

'Yeah, from Michael.'

Jacqui brought Evyn up their front steps, in out of the rain, and followed Kelly inside. 'What did Michael want?'

'I wasn't here when he called. He just left a message.'

'Can you pass me the phone? Weird that Michael called. When was the last time I heard from him?' Jacqui gently placed Evyn on the living room floor so she could play with her toys. She dialled the number Kelly had written down. He answered on the first ring.

'Hi, Michael. It's Jacqui. What's up?'

'Hi, Jacqui. Hi. Tess wanted me to let you know that there has been an accident. Zoë had a riding accident, and we're all at the hospital.'

'What? Is she OK? Can we see her?' Jacqui's mood abruptly darkened. Kelly's attention immediately shifted from Evyn to Jacqui.

Michael responded, 'She took a bad fall from her horse this morning. Hit her head. She's still unconscious but breathing on her own. They're only allowing family in right now.'

'She's unconscious! Oh, my God! How's Tess doing?'

By now Kelly had figured out something had happened to Zoë. Evyn was looking up from the floor. The baby had noticed that the energy had changed dramatically. She watched them with large blue eyes. Kelly bent down and scooped her up. They both looked expectantly at Jacqui.

'Tess is doing better. She fainted when she got to the hospital. I guess it was too much to take in. She is obviously concerned, but she'll be OK. Look, I need to get back to them. They don't really like you using a cell phone in the room. How about I give you a call when we get an update from the doctor, OK?' Michael wished he didn't have to make these calls. He just wanted to be with Tess and Zoë.

'Yeah, sure. Please keep in touch, Michael. And give all our love to Tess and Zoë. We'll be thinking of all of you.' Jacqui hung up and she slumped down on the couch.

Kelly asked, 'What happened to Zoë?'

'She fell off her horse. She's unconscious. Tess must be frantic.'

'Is there anything we can do?'

'I don't know. I don't know. We can't visit. I should call Ariana and Gabi. It's bad, Kel.'

'I know. I know.' Kelly turned towards Evyn. 'Baby, you're never getting on a horse. Do you hear me?'

Jacqui left the two of them and poured herself a glass of wine.

She took the glass to the kitchen table and began dialling Ariana's number.

≥♣.

That night Tess and Michael sat quietly beside Zoë. Michael was still. His smooth hand gently held Zoë's. Tess was moving. She kissed Zoë's forehead, lovingly caressed her arm, hand, legs, and feet. Ever so carefully, she brushed the hair from her eyes, ran her fingers along the line of her cheek, all the while whispering her abiding love, reassuring Zoë that she would be OK, that her mommy and daddy were both there, that they loved her.

'Do you want anything, Tess?' Michael placed Zoë's hand tenderly at her side on the cool white sheet and looked over at his wife. It was almost as if she didn't hear him.

'Tess ... Tess.' Michael moved around the bed and reached for Tess's hand. She robotically twisted it out of his grasp and continued stroking Zoë's hair, ignoring him.

'Tess, please. Tess, talk to me.'

'What do you want me to say, Michael?' Tess was quiet, never taking her eyes off Zoë.

'This is not my fault, Tess.'

'I never said that it was.'

'You're acting like I'm some sort of pariah. Tess, I need you, too. We need each other now. Don't shut me out.'

'This isn't about you, Michael.' Tess's voice was monotone.

'You know what, I'm going to get us some coffee. I'll be right back.' Michael turned to leave the room, clearly annoyed and feeling totally incapable of connecting with Tess. He was frustrated. He knew that now was not the time to start an argument, yet he needed her comfort. He, too, was afraid. For now, all their energies needed to be focused on Zoë.

Tess said nothing as he left. She didn't really understand why she had avoided his touch. Why did she feel so disconnected from him now? Perhaps she had for a long time and was only coming to realize it. But she felt nothing for him now. He seemed like a stranger to her. She lowered her head, laying it gently on Zoë's hand, and wearily shut her eyes, her tears trickling through closed eyelids. Whenever she moved, she could feel the tender spot on the back of her skull where her head had hit the floor earlier that day. It would have been much worse if the nurse hadn't been there to break her fall. So embarrassing to faint. She needed to be strong for Zoë. She would not leave this bedside until they could walk out of this hospital together. Tess thought of all the things she wanted to do with Zoë when she came home – take her to lunch at her favourite restaurant, Bell's, where Zoë always ordered a chocolate milkshake, cheeseburger, and chocolate mousse cake for dessert. When was the last time they went to Bell's? How skewed had Tess's priorities become? When did she forget what was most important in her life? Just as Tess began to slip into deep self-beratement, she heard a small voice and immediately lifted her head. All of a sudden her baby was awake and trying to talk.

'Oh, my God. Zoë? Zoë? You're alright, sweetheart. I'm here.' She held Zoë's hand tightly and while she tried to notify the nurse, fumbling with the call button.

'Mom? Mom, my head hurts.' Zoë's eyes opened gingerly, as she slowly lifted her free hand to her temple.

'I know, darling. You've had a bad spill. You're going to be just fine. I love you so much. Don't ever forget that. Oh, thank God!' Tess glanced skyward in relief and gratitude. Her prayers had been answered.

Just then the nurse entered Zoë's room and carefully took Zoë's hand to check her pulse. 'How ya doing, little one?'

'My head hurts. Can I have a drink of water?'

Tess reached to Zoë's bedside for a cup of ice-water and bent the straw to her lips. Zoë took a small sip, coughed, and then took another sip.

'Take it slow, Zoë.' Tess's eyes met Zoë's, and they smiled. And then more tears coursed down Tess's face.

'Ah, mom. I'm fine. Really. Geez, don't cry.' Zoë's voice was still weak. She didn't sound convincing. The nurse took her blood pressure and then popped a plastic tube into Zoë's mouth, under her tongue, to check her temperature.

'I know you're going to be fine, sweetie. I'm just relieved. We were worried. So worried. You've been sleeping for almost twelve hours.'

'I'm going to page Dr Zahn, and she should be here in a couple minutes to have a chat. Sound, OK, Zoë?' The nurse seemed satisfied with Zoë's vital signs and smoothed her bedding.

Zoë smiled, then winced. She was reminded instantly of where her own head had hit the ground.

'Just try to lay still, Zoë.' Tess looked to the nurse for reinforcement.

'That's a good idea. Listen to your mom, Zoë. I'll be back in a little while.' The nurse walked around the bed and smiled back at the two as she gently closed the door.

'Where's dad?'

'Oh, Michael!' It took a moment for her to recall where he had gone. 'Oh, he just went to get a coffee. He's going to be very excited to see you awake.'

'Mom, is Collage OK?' Collage was Zoë's favourite horse. Tess guessed it was Collage that Zoë was riding when she fell.

'I'm sure Collage is fine, darling. Right now, all we need to worry about is you.'

'Can you phone the stable and find out for me, mom? It wasn't his fault.' Zoë's eyes were pleading. She tried to sit up and realized she couldn't and then eased back into her pillow.

'I know, sweetheart. I'm not blaming Collage. It was an accident. Just an accident. I will phone in a little while, OK.'

Just then Michael rushed into the room, his face breaking into a huge smile when he saw Zoë.

'Hi, Dad!' Zoë's voice was light and carefree, no indication of the agony that she caused them.

'Oh, Zoë! What a sight for sore eyes you are.' Michael put

down two lattés on the bedside table and resumed his position on the opposite side of the bed from Tess. 'You had us quite worried, little bug. How's your head?'

'It's sore, Dad. It hurts when I move it.'

'Just be still, bug. Let's wait to hear from the doctor. Has she been by yet?' Michael looked across to Tess. Finally, their eyes met, and in each other they could see the reflection of their open hearts, graced by the deep gratitude of their daughter's awakening. Michael reached for Tess's hand and Zoë smiled.

Tess, grateful he was back, grateful her family was back, replied, 'No, she is on her way. They just paged her. Zoë wants to know when she can go home.'

'Oh, really? I'm not surprised.' Michael was relieved for many reasons.

Zoë, with all sincerity asked, 'Dad, what's a sight for sore eyes?'

Tess and Michael began to laugh, and their laughter eased the strain between them. Their eyes met briefly, tenderly, and then they both looked down at Zoë.

'What?' Zoë was unaware of the significance of their exchanged glance, but felt the safety of it still. 'You two are so weird!'

Tess's eyebrows raised and Michael shook his head. They looked across at each other again, *grieving for what they had done in the name of their own ascendancies and aspirations.* The relief of their reconnection started them off again until their laughter mingled with tears and they were weak in the grip of love.

Chapter Eleven – Tender Fear

It will take time to forgive myself and outlive
the hidden fears that lurk in moist eyecorners.

(Jardine, 1998, p. 139)

Week 11: November 16

The week was excruciating for Jacqui. Hearing Wednesday that Zoë was going to make a full recovery was the good news she needed to get her through. And today, she was standing before a concerned group of young women, self-deceived into thinking she could speak coherently on the topic of her recently completed doctoral research. Yesterday morning, Jacqui received an email from Alice asking if she would be willing to instruct the final few classes of the term.

'Sure, I'd be glad to help.' Jacqui responded. She thought she would be doing Tess a favour and was more than willing to step in for her.

'Would you like me to come by tomorrow to introduce you?' Alice asked.

Jacqui politely declined her offer. The formality seemed unnecessary.

'Alright, but would you mind mentioning to the students that Tess won't be returning? It will save me having to send them an email.'

Jacqui agreed and considered what she might say, but she was more preoccupied with wanting to connect with Tess and Zoë. The next twenty-four hours flew by as Jacqui read and re-read her class notes and printed out overhead transparencies.

And then Jacqui found herself in front of the students. It was 9 o'clock. Time to begin.

'Hi. My name is Jacqui. I guess we'll get started. But, uh, I suppose you might be wondering why Tess is not here today. Well, she's had a family emergency and she won't be returning to teach for the rest of the term.' A murmur went through the room. Meg sat not far from Dani and stared over at her thinking, 'Now you've got your wish.' Jacqui was completely oblivious to the growing tension between the two.

Marci in the front row, put up her hand and asked, 'Do we still have to hand in our assignment today?'

Before Jacqui could answer her question, Candice asked, 'Is there still going to be a final exam?'

Sammi, legs crossed, nonchalantly sipping from her stainless steel coffee mug asked, 'Are you taking over for the rest of the term?'

The questions slightly unnerved Jacqui. 'Actually, yes. I am.'

A student whispered indiscreetly to Dani, 'Two profs in one term. Lucky us.'

Jacqui took a breath and tried a slightly different tack, 'I realize that you're coming up to the end of the term and things are probably getting pretty intense for all of you, so let's try to get through this together. Yes, there's going to be a final exam for those electing that option. And, I will be marking term papers for those who elect that option. Oh, and your second assignment is due today. Any other questions?'

'Is Tess's daughter going to be OK?' Meg asked, very concerned.

Jacqui wondered how this student knew about Zoë. 'Yes, thank goodness, she is going to be completely fine. She gave us all quite a scare, but she will be fine. OK, why don't we take a look at this article that I'm planning to submit to the DC journal? I think it describes at least part of my research reasonably well, but I would just like to tell you a bit about what I had to leave out.'

Jacqui launched quickly into her lesson. 'First, I wasn't really able to go into the educational theory historically underlying dietetic education. Has anyone ever heard of Bloom or Bloom's taxonomy?'

Hardly waiting a second in her nervousness, she hurried on. 'No? OK. Basically, Bloom's philosophy of education is that if instructors provide a set of behavioural objectives, learning out-comes, or knowledge statements, the students' learning becomes quantifiable. When behavioural objectivism came about in the 1960s, it represented a turn away from dietetic education based on practical wisdom to education based on research. Cherryholmes says that behavioural objectives, including Bloom's taxonomy, are grounded in structuralist principles because they "promise order, organization, rationality, error correction, political neutrality, ex-pertise, and progress" (Cherryholmes, 1988, p. 26). Behavioural objectivism forced students to take more responsibility for their learning. Cherryholmes also says that the work of Bloom rests on unsound categories, has embedded within it ideology while denying ideological content, advances non-linear structures as linear, promotes unethical educational decision making, and ignores the political character of all argumentation. There are some academic folks, curricularists, who claim Bloom's work is not to be taken seriously (Pinar, Reynolds, Slattery, & Taubman, 2002). So, why am I making such a long-winded speech about Bloom? Well, dietetic education is based in part on what Bloom philosophized. So, if some think Bloom's work is not to be taken seriously, what does that mean for dietetic education?'

Jacqui paused and noticed a hand went up, 'Oh, good, a ques-tion. OK. Great.'

Sammi, not having moved since the start of the class, asked, 'Do we have to take notes on this?'

Jacqui smiled. 'You are welcome to do whatever best suits your own style of learning. Any other questions?'

Jacqui looked down at a pile of notes she had put together from her comprehensive exam papers. She wished she had put aside more time to plan this class, but her mind had been in a haze from what had happened in the preceding seven days. She went with her instincts. Looking up, she saw that there were no more obvious questions. Sammi still hadn't moved.

The second thing that I couldn't really elaborate on in my article was the theoretical lens through which I consider my research. It's called poststructuralism. Can anyone tell me what that means?' Jacqui waited. Again, no response.

'Alright. Generally, poststructuralists believe that individuals have agency to the degree that they are able to constitute discourse. Remember, though, that individuals are constituted by discourse. Poststructuralists believe that subjects don't exist outside discourse. Poststructuralists see the world as contextualized, that every person's knowledge is situated in their experience, and that one person's view can only be partial. In contrast, structuralism rejects the possibility of human experience impacting systems of order. Structuralists assert that structures exist as organizing centres of social action. So, how many of you would say that Bloom is a structuralist?'

Three quarters of the students raised their hands. 'You are correct. Now has anyone heard of Deborah Lupton?' Only Meg nodded.

'Lupton wrote a book called *Food, Body and the Self*. Excellent book. Highly recommend it.' Jacqui looked down and read directly from her notes. 'Like Lupton, I believe that it is "through discourses ... that individuals come to understand themselves, their bodies, and their relationship to food and eating"' (Lupton, 1996, p. 13). Looking up at the students again, she asked, 'Has Tess talked about discourse with you? Has that word come up?'

Some of the students nodded. Jacqui added, 'What is discourse then, anyone?'

Meg quickly offered, 'A specialized language used by experts and adopted by others to describe a very specific type of knowledge.'

'Good. Forgive me, but what's your name?' Jacqui asked.

Smiling, she answered, 'I'm Meg.'

'Hi, Meg.' Then turning to the rest of the students, Jacqui added, 'I do want to learn your names. Maybe if you have a question, just start with telling me your name. That would help. OK, so the way I understand dietetic education is that it is a process that generates knowledges about bodies and relationships to food and eating. I used to believe more strongly that individuals socialized dietetic students into the profession, but I've come to understand the process as more complicated and less deliberate than that.'

Jacqui continued the lecture. 'The third and final thing I would like to mention about my research is methodological. I wasn't able to fully explain my autoethnographic approach in this article. It's written as a more standard, traditional sociological discourse. Has anyone ever heard of autoethnography?'

No response. Jacqui was starting to feel just slightly uncomfortable with how her scholarly passions seemed so completely outside the experiences of these student-contemporaries. Or was the silence indicative of the teaching style she had inadvertently adopted this morning?

'Well, yes, it's not exactly a mainstream method! OK, I'm sure you've heard of autobiography.' A few heads nodded. 'Well, in it's most simple definition, autoethnography is an autobiographical tale written around a specific cultural location. For me, the culture I attempted to explore and illuminate is the culture of dietetics. So, autoethnography permits me to explore my identity as a dietitian within the culture of dietetics. I'm a researcher and participant. Carolyn Ellis, the scholar most closely associated with autoethnography, says that when it's done effectively, "autoethnography evokes in readers a feeling that the experience described is authentic, that it is believable and possible" (Ellis, 1995, p. 318-319).

Dani put up her hand, 'What are the ethics of that? I mean it sounds to me to be pretty biased.'

For the first time in the class, a student responded to another student's question. It was Meg. Her voice was uncharacteristically sharp. 'Dani, what would you know about ethics? Why don't you tell us your definition of ethics?' Meg's language was injurious. Dani was taken aback, defensive.

Jacqui was caught off guard. Where had she heard that name before? Dani?

'Whoa, Meg. Easy, girl. I just asked a simple question. What's your problem?' The class was locked in the tension between these two women.

'What's my problem? My problem? Actually, Dani, *you're* my problem.'

Dani was playing it cool. 'Look, I don't know what you're trying to say, but why don't you just come out with it. Say what you need to say.'

Jacqui finally regained her bearings. 'OK, uh, I'm not exactly sure what this is about, but maybe ...'

She was interrupted by Meg, who filled in some of the blanks with her excitable speech. Staring straight at Dani, with a strong, clear voice, and arms crossed, she responded, 'You know, this whole thing reeks of hypocrisy. Let's consider the ethics of complaining about your instructor behind her back. Let's consider the ethics of thinking this course isn't important to being a dietitian. Let's consider the ethics of starving yourself, but thinking it's OK to tell others how to eat healthy.'

A look of white shock registered across Dani's face. She immediately glanced towards the front of the class, and at that moment Jacqui remembered the email she received from Dani ten days ago. Before she could stop herself, Jacqui muttered, 'Dani Sutherland. You're Dani Sutherland.' Dani's vulnerability turned to anger, and she jumped up out of her chair, the force sending it back into the wall. Startled by the crashing chair, the other students jumped. No one intervened as Dani rushed towards Meg, a look of sheer rage on her face. In the few seconds it took Dani to cross the room, Meg was also standing. When she reached Meg, Dani, fists clenched, hissed in a furious whisper, 'You bitch.' Meg looked terrified and wisely she said nothing.

Jacqui stepped towards Meg and Dani, but before she reached them Dani turned and bolted from the room, slamming the door behind her.

'Dani! Wait!' Jacqui was helpless. She stood beside Meg as they both watched her leave.

Meg, biting the corner of her trembling lip, said quietly, 'Let her go. Obviously, the truth hurts.'

Jacqui wondered what had just happened. It seemed like a rug was pulled out from under her. What was she going to do?

'Is there someone who can go check on Dani, just to be with her and make sure she's OK?'

'I'll go.' Sammi put down her coffee cup and stood to leave, shooting an accusing look towards Meg as she walked past.

'OK, thanks. If you can, please come back before the end of class and let me know if she's OK.' Jacqui tried to collect her thoughts. 'And everyone else, if you could please take your seats for a moment. I'd like to get a sense of what's happening here. I mean, I'm feeling kind of in the dark.'

Jacqui sank into an empty seat and the students reluctantly rearranged themselves to face her.

Meg began apologizing, 'I'm sorry, guys. I guess that wasn't too appropriate, was it?'

Candice weighed in, 'Uh, that was pretty intense. I mean, what's up with you two?'

'You know, it's, it's just … I don't know where that came from.' Then Meg once again surprised everyone and began to cry.

Jacqui wondered if things could get any worse.

'Alright, ladies. My goodness! Poststructuralism doesn't usually have this effect on people.' Jacqui tried to bring levity to a situation that was well beyond her attempts at humour. She tried again. 'Let's all take one deep breath, OK?'

The women collectively breathed in, then out. An athletic-looking student wearing a Nike baseball cap pulled low put her arm around Meg's shoulder, in an attempt to offer some comfort. They were all looking to Jacqui for what to do next.

Jacqui felt burdened by having to say and do something, but then finally just gave in to authenticity. 'I don't know about the rest of you, but this has been one hell of a week for me and I sure wish Tess were here. She'd know what to say.' Her shoulders slumped and her professional veneer disappeared.

Meg, through her tears, said to everyone and nobody in particular, 'I wish she was here, too.'

The student comforting Meg added, 'What happened last week with Dr Taylor coming in here and pulling Tess into the hall, it was brutal. We could hear everything. We felt so bad for Tess. Then class was just cancelled, like nobody even bothered to, like, explain what was happening.'

Jacqui started to understand where some of the tension began. The experience last week was clearly traumatizing for Tess's students.

Jacqui realized her responsibility to these young women even though they didn't know each other well. 'I'm really sorry you've been left in the dark. Tess is a close friend, so I know she would be sorry to hear this, too. It would be honest to say Tess's been in a bit of a different headspace since the moment she heard Zoë was taken to the hospital.'

Meg begin to relax and stopped crying. 'Is there any way we can contact her, send her a card or something?'

'Of course. That would be an incredibly kind gesture. Uh, would you like to put something together for her right now and I can take it to her when class is done?'

Jacqui noticed several students nodding in agreement. 'OK, great. Just take whatever time you need right now and feel free to go when you're finished. There will be a class next week and I think it will be very good to come together and talk about Freshwater's article in particular. Does that sound alright?'

Many students were already pulling out paper and beginning to write. Jacqui said nothing more and quietly left them to find Dani and the other student. She was more than a little worried about Dani and could only imagine the humiliation she might be feeling. Because of her work with women who struggle with food and body distrust, Jacqui knew she must bring delicate care and sensitivity to her conversation with Dani. And this could be an opportunity, a chance for her and each and every student in that class to learn how to respond to shame and vulnerability and other strong emotions. These were the lessons of an embodied curriculum (Norman, 1995). These were the lessons of cultural sensitivity, of engaged pedagogy (hooks, 2003). These were some of the most important self-orientations they could engage with in their preparation for their work as dietitians. Jacqui steadied herself for the inevitable.

&.

Jacqui knocked gently on Tess's front door. She carried with her the messages from Tess's students. Zoë arrived home from the hospital on Friday, four days ago. Although she had spoken with them on the phone over the weekend, this would be the first time Jacqui had seen Tess since the accident. She was excited to be delivering good wishes from students. She hoped they would lift Tess's spirits.

Tess answered Jacqui's knock. She was dressed in the comfort of purple drawstring pyjama pants and a white cotton T-shirt. She was smiling and warmly welcomed Jacqui into their home with a generous hug. Jacqui could smell chicken soup and heard Evanescence coming from the stereo. Around the corner, Zoë was propped up on the couch, surrounded by magazines and quilts and pillows. She was smiling, too.

'Hey, Jacq! I'd get up, but Mom would freak. How's it going?'

'Good, Zoë, good. How are you, girl?' Jacqui placed her bag on the foyer floor and entered the living room, as she handed her coat to Tess.

'Well, I'm totally fine. It's my mom. She thinks I'm some kind of fragile doll. She's fully into the nurse role, and the police role, and the cook role. Isn't that what dietitians do, Jacq? Cook?'

Zoë had a mischievous sparkle in her eyes. She knew that was a sore point for some dietitians. To cook or not to cook?

'Never too cool to cook! Hey, we police and nurse, too! Actually, I wouldn't be pushing it, Zoë. How long do you think this will last, all this divine attention?'

'Forever, I hope. Hey, Mom, you can quit your job, too and we can all just hang out together.'

Tess fluffed up Zoë's pillows much like a nurse might do and was unapologetic in her caring, 'I'm not going to quit my job. Just taking a week right now to be here with you. There's nowhere else I'd rather be. You're stuck with me. Tough!'

Jacqui noticed that Michael wasn't around but didn't bother to ask about him. She sensed this might change the upbeat mood she had walked in on, and it felt so good, especially considering the pain of the last seven days.

Zoë asked, 'How's Evyn? Walking yet?'

'Not quite. Crawling and standing up, but not walking. Won't that be fun? Kelly and I already tried to baby-proof the living room, but she still finds things. She's a smart one. Very clever. Just like you.'

Tess, finished fussing over Zoë for the moment, rose and asked Jacqui if she wanted some tea.

'Sure, that would be great. Any matcha?' she replied, laughing.

'No, matcha, my dear, only Tetley.'

'Tetley it is. Have you tried matcha yet Zoë?'

Jacqui and Zoë could hear Tess in the kitchen making tea, arranging goodies, being a good mother-dietitian.

'Uh, no! What's matcha?'

'Oh, it's pretty intense. Supposed to be good for you!'

'I'm sure Mom will be forcing me to drink it any day, then. Jacq, she's out of control.'

'You're going to have to forgive her, Zoë. She was beside herself when she found out you fell. It's going to take some time for her to settle down. Pretty tough being loved so much, hey!' Jacqui poked fun at Zoë.

'Yeah, look around. It really sucks!' Clearly Zoë was content and would find the strength somewhere deep inside herself to permit her mom to pamper her for the remainder of her time off.

Tess returned to the living room with peach cobbler and a tray of tea. 'Do you want soup first or cobbler, Zoë?'

'Since when do I get dessert before lunch, Mom? Soup, please.'

'Your mom is a good dietitian. She knows it does no good to hold the dessert out as a reward. Don't knock it, Zoë!' Jacqui helped Tess clear a space on the coffee table for her decadent tray.

'Hey, Tess, I brought some things for you from the students.'

Tess carefully passed Zoë a large bowl of steaming soup. 'What? Their assignments to mark?'

'No, unless you want to mark them! Actually, they were really distraught after Alice came into the class last week and you left to go to the hospital. They needed to be in touch with you, so we did some writing.' Jacqui leaned over and put her tea on a side table and then picked up her bag, pulling out a generous stack of papers and handed them to Tess.

'Oh, my goodness. I didn't expect this. They didn't have to do this!'

'Tess, they *needed* to do this.'

'That's so kind of them.' Tess began to read and then put the pages down on the table beside the tray. 'I can't read these right now. I'll cry.'

'Oh, my God, Mom! No more crying. That's all she ever does now, Jacq. It's totally embarrassing. Mom, please, please, when my friends come over later, please don't cry. It's ridiculous!'

Tess laughed. 'OK, Zoë. I'll be discreet. I'll only drink and smoke and swear. I won't cry. OK?'

'Oh, Mom!'

Jacqui watched the two of them teasing each other. She was moved with the relief that their worlds hadn't been too drastically altered. She felt a profound gratitude for her life, the life of Kelly and Evyn, the life of her friends.

Tess's voice interrupted Jacqui's thoughts. 'Thanks so much for agreeing to take over the last three weeks of class for me, Jacqui. I really appreciate it. I thought for a moment about trying to do it all, and then I came to my senses. I can't do it all. I don't want to do it all. Why do we think we have to be all things to all people? Work has been great. Everyone has been so supportive. I think there are going to be some changes for me when I go back. For sure. Hey, Zoë?'

'Mom wants to start riding with me. How cool is that?'

'Pretty cool, Zoë. Wow! Can I come and take pictures?' Jacqui looked over at Tess, her eyebrows raised in surprise. Tess shrugged.

'Yeah, that's right. I can ride. Why don't you come sometime, too, Jacq. Didn't you ride when you were younger?'

'Yeah, I rode. It's been a while.'

'You used to ride? Really? English?' Zoë put her soupspoon down for a moment.

'Uh-huh. I used to do eventing with my horse Afarasta, Ruffy for short. A beautiful white Arab. Dressage, cross-country, and stadium jumping. Oh, those were good times.'

Good times, indeed. Jacqui, Tess, and Zoë slipped into a lively conversation about horses and riding and falling off and getting back on. Falling off and getting back on. A perfect description of their lives, and they wouldn't have it any other way.

❧

Jacqui looked back over her shoulder at Tess standing by her front door and waved. It was good to have spent some time with them. She hoped to visit again soon, perhaps with Kelly and Evyn. Evyn at this age was incredibly entertaining, and as long as she had her naps and enough food, everyone was happy. As Jacqui walked to the bus stop, her thoughts again returned to the research workshop transcripts, an endless preoccupation. She had been remembering lately the closing ritual she performed on a whim with participants at that final group. Nancy had asked her what she thought the barriers to change were in dietetic education. Jacqui had responded with a quote from poet Muriel Rukeyser, *the emotional obstacle is the real one* (Rukeyser, 1996, p. 13). And she asked the participants to fill their glasses. She wanted to propose a toast. She had been rereading the transcripts late the night before and could hear her own voice.

'I invite you to stand with me. Please join me in a toast of welcome to our newest colleague, Yasma, who today officially passed her dietetics exam and is a full-fledged dietitian!' Jacqui remembered raising her plastic cup and hearing the muting clicks as everyone brought their cups together. There was a brief moment of quiet while everyone took a sip of their drink. And then Jacqui realized that her initial words didn't convey the depth of meaning the moment required, so she added, 'Hearing your story, hearing how you came to us from Iran, and what you had to go through to get to this moment afforded me a profound sense of sadness, but also inspiration. I honour you in your incredible spirit.' Jacqui briefly caught Valerie's eyes and was surprised to see tears forming. Instantly, Jacqui connected with strong feelings of her own. Speaking slowly and more quietly, she continued. 'I have to say …' she paused and sighed heavily, aware that she was going to become incredibly vulnerable if she continued. 'It's very emotional,' her voice finally breaking, her own tears breaking, her eyes shifted away from Yasma, cast downwards, letting the tears fall. Jacqui could hear Valerie's voice. 'We don't make it easy.'

Jacqui was aware that the others in the room had a limited sense of what Yasma had been through, of the rules, of the strife, of the arbitrary manoeuvres to become a Canadian dietitian. There was silence on the tapes as Jacqui over and over felt the rush of self-gratitude that she had made that toast and made visible even to those few in the room that which usually went unnoticed and remained invisible. She believed that as dietitians, if they were truly about creating places for people to be healthy, they would never place up such roadblocks to their own colleagues. But it happened and would continue to happen until they made it be different. She realized then that it would take time, lots of time, for the profession, for each of them, to *forgive themselves and outlive the hidden fears that lurk in moist eyecorners.*

Chapter Twelve – Sweet Fruits

... although reflection is an individual process,
the capacity of human beings for reflection
is premised on intersubjectivity.
The embracing of subjectivity ...
does not necessarily lead to individualism;
indeed, it uncovers the social in human experience.

(Crawford et al., 1992, p. 117)

Week 12: November 23

'I'd like to start with a poem. I have great faith that poetry can help us heal our wounds, so I think a poem is appropriate for us today.'

Jacqui was holding a single sheet of paper in her hands. She waited another moment while several more students made their way to their desks.

'The poem is called "All That Is Good".'

> *'I'm passionate about what I do.'*
>> *yes, you are*
>> *I read your passion like text*
>> *a light that sparks your eyes*
>> *lit by faith*
> *alive*

> *'I'm centred in the client'*
> *your passion for equality*
>> *fairness*
>> *in tune, harmony*
> *an ethics unbounded*
>> *artfully respectful*
>> *irreverently political*

integrity of white lights
illuminating our way
we are cradled in your integrity

'We have a bigger voice.'
strong sure feelings
advocate of the heart
connected to community
feel the pulse of humanity
hands in so many pies
taste the fruits of your labour
sweet fruits of your passion

you are cherished, dear woman
here, today always
in your visions of tomorrow
calm, spiritual
and good
yes, you are all that is good
you cradle us here
close to the bone
a heart that is filled
with all that is good

Jacqui paused momentarily before she offered a bit of context for the poem. 'I wrote this for a dietitian, a co-participant in my research. For me the sentiment expressed here speaks to the power of relationship, of coming to understand another. You see, before I started my research, I had many misgivings about my colleagues and about my profession. I seem to recall Tess having mentioned to you early in the term about our profession dying. Well, I *yearned* for our profession to die. I could see only pain being caused by dietitians; pain to their clients, pain to their colleagues, and pain to themselves. I placed much of the blame for such a dire situation on the way we were educated. And, I still believe there is much we can do to improve the way we

educate each other, but I've come to realize that in addition to
the pain, there is profound love and overwhelming passion. In
working with my research participants, my colleagues, I came to
understand these women as beings with inordinately complex
lives. I came to understand that we're all living with effects of
what Freshwater calls a 'system that has excluded us from power'
(Freshwater, 2006). So, I share this with you in light of what happened in this classroom last week as a way for us to acknowledge
the pain, to begin to heal the shame of secrecy, and to celebrate
our passion for our work and for each other. I think I'd like to
open it up now for some feedback from you about how we might
go about doing this.'

The students were subdued. The events of the previous week
were still fresh in their hearts. They didn't feel entirely safe venturing into such personal and emotionally laden conversations.

Sammi, a typically brave student, ventured a comment. 'You
know, I was really surprised to read of horizontal violence in
nursing. I was thinking of Tess when I read this sentence, page
483.' Some of the students flipped through the article to that
page. Sammi began to read. '"Such education suppresses the
imagination of the student and their capacity to dream is substi-
tuted by the capacity to live out someone else's dream." Tess did
the opposite. I think from the very beginning she sparked my
imagination.'

Candice shared her insights, 'Maybe that's where the conflict
came from. We're not accustomed to change. Like this Farmer
quote in the article, "It's easier to continually resort to horizontal
violence than to make meaningful changes." I think that says it
all.'

Jacqui noticed that Meg and Dani were not making eye contact with each other. They were sitting as far apart as the room
would allow. Neither of them had spoken.

The athletic-looking student, this time wearing a grey hat with
the word 'Ping' written across it in bold red letters, wasn't convinced. 'It seems easier to me to just take notes and get on with

it. No emotions, no conflict. That's too hard. It's too upsetting. People can get hurt.'

Jacqui was aware she wanted to rise to the defence of emancipatory education. She waited instead.

Finally Meg decided she could stay silent no longer. 'I think I should say something. I've been waiting to say it in person.' Meg turned in her chair to face Dani. 'It was never my intention to hurt you, Dani. I wish I could take back what I said, but I can't. It's out there now. I regret it. I want to tell you that I'm sorry. I'm very sorry.' Dani didn't look at Meg. Jacqui knew Dani almost didn't come to class today. She had spent the better part of an hour with Dani yesterday afternoon trying to convince her to attend. Jacqui was pleased that she was there, but it was clear that an overwhelming, supreme tension existed between the two.

Jacqui thought it was her turn. 'I believe there is a consequence to not expressing emotion and not acknowledging emotion in the classroom. I think part of what happened last week is the consequence of unexpressed conflict, ironically. Many of you won't believe this, but dietetics is an oppressed group. We are oppressed by our gender and oppressed by our place in the medical hierarchy. We express conflict in hurtful ways because of that oppression. A philosopher named Judith Butler calls this mundane violence. We hurt others and we hurt ourselves. What I hear Freshwater saying is that it doesn't have to be that way. For it to be otherwise, she suggests that, in addition to learning about reflective practice, we must consider social change, we must resist the double bind that Travers says we will find ourselves in (Travers, 1995). You've read her work, right? She suggests that if we don't become aware of the bigger world around us and the inequities in our world, we will perpetuate those inequities. And I know we don't want to do that.'

The students listened quietly. One doodled in her notebook.

Knowing the class was to end soon, Jacqui felt compelled to link their discussion to the last article. 'Given what Freshwater suggests as a direction for us to take, towards transformative education, what ideal do Thomas and Smith propose would be the result? I would like you to take ten minutes right now and respond in writing, or a poem, or a drawing, or whatever, to the question, which I believe is an important question, What is your ideal of the person educated in dietetics?'

The students didn't respond with much enthusiasm to Jacqui's invitation. Maybe she rushed the conversation they were having. Jacqui tried to add an incentive. 'This will be your final reader-response for the term.'

Jacqui's motivation didn't seem to have the desired effect, but slowly the students began to write. Maybe they were all relieved not to be talking for the time being.

After ten minutes, Jacqui asked, 'Would anyone be willing to share what she's written?'

Meg, who may have felt largely unburdened after apologizing publicly to Dani, raised her hand.

'Meg, great. Please go ahead.'

'OK. So, it's pretty short. Uh, an ideal of a person educated in dietetics is how that person cares about others and how she initiates conversations and how she looks at her own mistakes and makes amends for those mistakes. That's it.'

Meg was clearly still trying to apologize.

'Thanks, Meg. Any others?'

The athletic student volunteered. 'Yeah, like the ideal of some-one educated is for that person to always think about how her actions affect those around her. It's about trying to do something positive for others and not just using them as a means for an end, like trying to make money off people who need help. I think it's mostly about learning to walk in someone else's shoes, but having the knowledge to understand what makes it difficult to walk in that person's shoes at that time in their life. Like, you know, the social theory stuff.'

'Nice. I really like how you said that.' Jacqui put a transparency on the overhead projector.

'I've given this question considerable thought, too, and before

I share my writing with you, I would like to share a quote from a man named Ted Aoki, who also describes this ideal quite beautifully.

Jacqui turned on the projector and the students began to read.

Toward an Ideal of the Person Educated in Dietetics:

> The educated person … understands that one's ways of knowing, thinking, and doing flow from who one is. Such a person knows that an authentic person is no mere individual … but a being-in-relation with others and at core, an ethical being. Such a person knows that being an educated person is more than possessing knowledge or acquiring managerial skills; that being an educated person is dwelling aright in thoughtful living with others. The educated person not only guards against disembodied forms of knowing, thinking, and doing that reduce self and others to things, but also strives, guided by the authority of the good in pedagogical situations, for embodied thoughtfulness that makes possible living as human beings. Moreover, the educated person speaks and acts from a deep sense of humility, conscious of the limits set by human finitude and morality, acknowledging the grace by which educator and educated are allowed to dwell in the present that embraces past experiences and is open to the possibilities yet to be. Thus, to be educated is to be ever open to the call of what it is to be deeply human, and heeding that call, to walk with others in life's ventures (Aoki, 1987, p. 23).

'Ted Aoki is clearly an incredible poet. I think the other question we share the responsibility for asking is "How have our educational experiences in dietetics encouraged us to be ever open to the call of what it means to be deeply human?" What does this mean to you, this question?'

Jacqui once again opened the class to discussion. As the students shared one after the other, Jacqui's thoughts drifted to Ellsworth's article, 'Why Doesn't This Feel Empowering' (Ellsworth, 1989)? With the voice of each of the women in that classroom sounding stronger and more impassioned about their future, Jacqui felt empowered. She felt hopeful and was immediately aware of a growing surge of joy spreading through her chest. It was the same feeling she had had when she was working with a woman in her practice and there had been a breakthrough, an insight, a deeply profound moment of mutual connection. Jacqui knew that the relationships she had with those women, with these students, and with herself were her response to what it meant to be *ever open to the call of what it is to be deeply human.* Like Ellsworth she believed it was possible to teach dietetic students in a way that doesn't require them to assume a fixed, singular, unified position within power and social relations (Ellsworth, 1997, p. 9). Eros, passion, and connection, all powerfully capable of disrupting the notion of a fixed identity and making it difficult to dehumanize others (Burch, 2000). Her joy came when eros was privileged. And then, in an unexpected memory, Jacqui heard the words of Lorde, the writing she was introduced to years earlier in Rishma's class. *Once we know that of which we are capable of feeling that sense of satisfaction and completion, we can then observe which of our various life endeavors bring us closest to that fullness.* And she knew that in this classroom, with these tender young women, speaking the truths of their lives, of work done and work yet to do, she was brought closest to that fullness. She was home.

ॐ

November 27

Dear Judith,

I've had a really difficult couple of weeks, but my psychic discomfort has been strangely productive. In class this week I shared a poem I had written during my research. I wrote the poem to honour my colleague, Harjeet, and the time we had spent together in conversation about what it means to be a dietitian, among many other things. When I offered Harjeet that poem, she passed it back to me and asked me to read it to her. As I read I became aware that she began to cry, and I was so moved by her tears that I began to cry, too. When I finished reading I felt so vulnerable. I didn't know what to say. Through her tears, Harjeet thanked me and then leaned forward with open arms and we embraced. We held each other for what seemed a long time before our tears subsided. Afterwards Harjeet told me no one had ever before written her a poem. I just remember her eyes, still moist from crying, soulful. I felt sure her eyes were saying as much as her words and I read my despair, my ache, my sadness there. I was profoundly humbled by that experience. My body became still and my mind quiet. I will never forget that moment we shared and I have my anger to thank I suppose.

I needed this research to learn of the Other. You remind me of this. This work has exposed realities to which I thought I was confined, but which inexplicably opened to transformation – my own and Others'. Before this research process began, the norm of dietetic practice felt constraining to me, dehumanizing. My anger with this norm became overly consuming; it is what I needed to live, and it threatened to efface me (Butler, 2004, p. 217). I suffered in my resistance, in my anger, and in my self-righteousness. Most profoundly, Harjeet's response to my poem undid me, filled me with humility. My anger dissolved. I felt it in my body, a shift.

Perhaps this is akin to the process you describe occurring when subject and Other understand themselves to be reflected in one another – recognition. This process is not a collapse of one into the Other and not a projection that annihilates the alterity of the Other (Butler, 2004, p. 132). I was transformed by virtue of the communicative practice in which I was engaged with Harjeet and our histories, and our bodies, our feelings, our desire, our longing for recognition. I became aware that we were both longing for recognition.

You write that it is at a moment of fundamental vulnerability that recognition becomes possible, and need becomes self-conscious (Butler, 2004, p. 149). I know what you speak of now. I understand that such recognition holds destruction and aggression in check. I was given over to reciprocity and mutuality. I consider such an experience as sacred. I don't know how you might respond to the notion of recognition as sacred, but I do know that moment of relationality is entitled to reverence and respect, a divine experience.

In what started as an effort to show how power and knowledges work to constitute dietetic practice, I've become otherwise. I've become wise to the knowledges and power that reside within Others and how our agentive task requires us to follow the points, which indicate their emergence (Butler, 2004, p. 215). Through this experience of being with colleagues engaged similarly and politically with the norms of and hopes for dietetic practice, I've recovered myself longing for recognition, less likely to anger, open to exceed the norm, rework the norm. Open to question.

In-complete,
Jacqui

Course Outline

Nutrition 430: Orientations to Dietetic Practice

Date	Week	Theme	Readings
Sept. 7	1	Introduction	
Sept. 14	2	The Power of Discourse I	Travers, K. D. (1995). 'Do you teach them how to budget?' Professional discourse in the construction of nutritional inequities. In D. Maurer & J. Sobal (Eds.), *Eating agendas: food and nutrition as social problems*. (pp. 213–240). New York: Aldine de Gruyter.
Sept. 21	3	The Power of Discourse II	Austin, S. B. (1999). Commodity knowledge in consumer culture: the role of nutritional health promotion in the making of the diet industry. In J. Sobal & D. Maurer (Eds.), *Weighty issues: fatness and thinness as social problems*. (pp. 159–181). New York: Aldine de Gruyter.
Sept. 28	4	Social Organization of the Profession	Liquori, T. (2001). Food matters: changing dimensions of science and practice in the nutrition profession. *Journal of Nutrition Education and Behaviour*, 33(4), 234–246.
Oct. 5	5	Becoming a Professional Assignment 1 Due	DeVault, M. (1999). Whose science of food and health? Narratives of profession and activism from public health nutrition. In *Liberating method: feminism and social research*. (pp. 139–155). Philadelphia: Temple University Press.

Date	Week	Theme	Readings
Oct. 12	6	What Counts as Nutrition Knowledge	Buchanan, D. (2004). Two models for defining the relationship method meeting our needs? *Journal of Nutrition Education and Behaviour*, 36(3), 146–154.
Oct. 19	7	Professional Ethics I	Martinez, R. (2000). Professional role in health care institutions: toward an ethic of authenticity. In D. Wear & J. Bickel (Eds.), *Educating for professionalism: creating a culture of humanism in medical education.* (pp. 35–48). Iowa City: University of Iowa Press.
Oct. 26	8	Professional Ethics II	Gingras, J. (2005). Evoking trust in the nutrition counsellor: why should we be trusted? *Journal of Agricultural and Environmental Ethics*, 18, 57–74.
Nov. 2	9	Professional Ethics III	Gussow, J. D. (1999). Dietary guidelines for sustainability: twelve years later. *Journal of Nutrition Education and Behaviour*, 31(4), 194–200.
Nov. 9	10	Revisiting Discourse	Travers, K. D. (1995). 'Do you teach them how to budget?' Professional discourse in the construction of nutritional inequities. In D. Maurer & J. Sobal (Eds.), *Eating agendas: food and nutrition as social problems.* (pp. 213–240). New York: Aldine de Gruyter.
Nov. 16	11	Performing 'Nutrition Expert' Assn 2 Due	Gingras, J. (in preparation). *The passion and melancholy of performing dietitian.*

Date	Week	Theme	Readings
Nov. 23	12	Future Considerations for Dietetic Education & Practice	Freshwater, D. (2000). Crosscurrents: against cultural narration in nursing. *Journal of Advanced Nursing, 32*(2), 481–484.
			Thomas, J., & Smith, G. (1994). Toward an ideal of the person educated in home economics: an invitation to dialogue. *Canadian Home Economics Journal, 44*(1), 20–25.
Nov. 30	13	Peer Debriefing & Exam Prep	

Course Glossary[2]

Capitalism A form of economic and social organization that has profit seeking as its goal. (p. 56)

Commodification A process where commodities (objects) are produced for the purpose of exchange. Often associated with capitalism since the exchange of commodities typically realizes a profit to the 'seller.' (p. 95)

Discourse A series of representations, practices, and performances through which meanings are produced, connected into networks, and legitimized. Discourses are heterogeneous, regulated, embedded, situated, and performative. (p. 180)

Ethics The systematic study of morality, concerned with what it is to make a moral judgement, which involves reasoned, consistent, and conclusive evaluation of good or bad, better or worse. (p. 231)

Feminism Theoretical perspectives that are critical of sexism, consider knowledge as situated, and consider the interconnections between all aspects of daily life. (p. 259)

Human Agency The capabilities of human beings, which some would argue is 'fundamentally illusory' if there is no subject outside of discourse. If a human does not exist outside of discourse can that person have the capacity to act? Agency may be more aptly recognized as *authority* given the power of discourse to constitute and subvert. (p. 349)

Ideology A system of ideas embedded in discourse that sustains power through the use of those ideas in the pursuit of particular interests, truths, and knowledges. (p. 369-370)

Patriarchy A system of social structures and practices through which women are dominated, oppressed, and exploited. Generally a subject of feminist critique. (p. 574-575)

---

[2] Definitions are sourced from Johnston, Gregory, Pratt, & Watts (2000) unless otherwise noted. Page numbers after definition refers to location in Johnston, et al (2000).

Performativity   An act that performs the action to which it refers. A model for thinking of identity formation and social processes in general. (p. 578)

Post-modernism   A philosophical movement characterized by scepticism towards grand claims of the modern era whereby interpretations are considered socially constituted, contingent, and partial. Postmodern positions stress an openness to a range of voice and perspectives. (p. 620)

Post-structuralism   Invites an openness to the unexpected, turns a critical gaze towards oppressive patterns of power and powerlessness, and engages a strong will to action (Davies, 2000, p. 170).

Power   The ability of a subject to achieve certain ends. (p. 629)

Resistance   A subject's response to domination or oppression that emerges through networks of power and knowledge. (p. 705)

Subjectification   Entails a tension between simultaneously becoming a speaking, agentic subject and being subjected to the meanings inherent in the discourse through which one becomes a subject (Davies, 2000, p. 27).

Subjectivity   Constituted through those discourses in which the person is being positioned at any one point in time, both through their own and others' acts of speaking/writing. Subjectivity is necessarily contradictory…and outside of or larger than those aspects of being that come under rational or conscious control (Davies, 2000, p. 57).

Epilogue

Tess was to teach Nutrition 430 only once more before program administrators decided to restructure the class as an interdisciplinary seminar on social issues in healthcare. Faculty from nursing, medicine, and occupational therapy joined Tess as co-instructors. Tess and Michael eventually started admitting the strain on their relationship. Although Tess would have preferred to see a counsellor to work through their issues, Michael refused. Still, she hoped that they would be able to resolve the tension between them. After several years, though, Tess and Michael decided to divorce. Tess and Zoë moved to the suburbs to be closer to Zoë's beloved horse, Collage. Tess accepted a part-time job in public health so she would have time to ride with her daughter.

Dani began her internship in a large urban hospital the year after graduating from dietetics. Not long after Tess's class ended, Dani came to realize the importance of healing her own relationship with food before beginning her counselling work with others, and she began therapy. She was hired on after her internship in the hospital's eating disorder clinic, where she continued to work full-time before leaving temporarily to give birth to the first of two children with her husband, Trevor, a professional hockey player. When Tess moved from the city after her divorce became final, she recommended Dani to take her place as guest speaker in the interdisciplinary seminar on social issues in healthcare. Dani was honoured and a little overwhelmed by Tess's invitation but pleased to be able to share Tess's teachings all these years later when Dani had finally realized their significance. Dani held her students' rapt attention with stories of her experience as an undergraduate. Her students loved her stories considerably more than her pop quizes!

Meg was thrilled to be accepted into a community nutrition internship after graduating from dietetics. Immediately following her internship, she sought a position with an international aid society and left Canada for Afghanistan. Meg wrote to Tess often about her work, describing the difficult conditions for women and children, especially the lack of access to education. She sometimes sent pictures of herself smiling brilliantly, wrapped in her trademark scarves, surrounded by the people she had grown to love and who obviously cared for her very much. Over the years, Meg's letters came less often until they eventually stopped altogether. One day, Tess recognized Meg in a newspaper photo as one of the people missing after a civilian aid bus had been ambushed by insurgents. Meg's whereabouts remain a mystery.

Gabrielle was married the very next year to Brent, a mechanical engineer. Less than six months later, she gave birth to Ethan and decided not to return to work after her maternity leave. Even though she had left dietetics, Gabi continued to meet with her friends for their facilitated support group. Three years later, Gabi published her first cookbook for kids and went on to write three more, becoming somewhat of a national cookbook celebrity. Her photo on the most recent cookbook's back cover shows her surrounded by dozens of children, all of them eating peanut butter and jelly sandwiches. Her joy is unmistakable.

Ariana continued to write and publish her poetry, performing readings on several occasions that Tess, Gabi, and Jacqui attended ardently. Her running brought her as much acclaim as her poetry. She went on to win the City Classic for three straight years. In time the dietetic profession named Ariana as recipient of the prestigious Marly-Greg award, an honour bestowed on dietitians who have made significant contributions to the profession. Ariana was recognized for her germinal theories on shame as an organizing feature of dietetic practice. Ariana astonished the audience when, instead of reading her acceptance speech, she performed it using movement, art, poetry, and a fabric collage that she entitled 'About Face: It's Not Meant to Be Beautiful.' She received a standing ovation from her peers.

Jane was admitted to the Clinical Eating Disorder Program and continued down the long road of recovery. She eventually finished her education degree and, immediately after graduating, accepted a teaching position in a small farming community far north of the city. Jane and Rachel began an intimate relationship soon after Jane completed school. They now live together on a hobby farm growing organic vegetables, which they harvest in such abundance that they arranged to sell some to the local grocer. Jane's brother, Brandon, lives just a few miles away with his wife, Sylvie, and their four children. Every Sunday morning Jane, Rachel, Brandon, Sylvie, and the kids attend church together.

Jacqui continued to write, teach, and support women struggling with eating and body issues. Not long after her doctorate, Jacqui began offering support groups for dietitians so they could work through some of their practice dilemmas together. Jacqui and Kelly eventually welcomed a sibling for Evyn. After Lewis was born, Jacqui became a stay-at-home mommy while Kelly accepted a full-time job managing a bakery.

Bibliography

Aoki, T. (1987). The educated person. *The BC Teacher, 67*(1), 23.

Baker Miller, J., & Pierce Stiver, I. (1997). *The healing connection: how women form relationships in therapy and in life.* Boston: Beacon Press.

Bateson, M. C. (1989). *Composing a life.* New York: Atlantic Monthly Press.

Billow, R. M. (2003). *Relational group psychotherapy: from basic assumptions to passion.* London, England: Jessica Kingsley Publishers.

Buchanan, D. (2004). Two models for defining the relationship between theory and practice in nutrition education: is the scientific method meeting our needs? *Journal of Nutrition Education and Behavior, 36*(3), 146-154.

Burch, K. T. (2000). *Eros as the educational principle of democracy.* New York: Peter Lang.

Butler, J. (1991). Imitation and gender insubordination. In D. Fuss (Ed.), *inside/out: lesbian theories, gay theories* (pp. 13-31). New York: Routledge.

Butler, J. (1997). *The psychic life of power: theories in subjection.* Stanford, CA: Stanford University Press.

Butler, J. (1999a). A 'bad writer' bites back. *The New York Times,* p. A15.

Butler, J. (1999b). Butler writes back. *New York Times.*

Butler, J. (1999c). *Gender trouble: feminism and the subversion of identity.* New York: Routledge.

Butler, J. (2004). *Undoing gender.* New York: Routledge.

Cherryholmes, C. (1988). *Power and criticism: poststructural investigations in education.* New York: Teachers College Press.

Choo, C. W. (1998). *The knowing organization: how organizations use information to construct meaning, create knowledge, and make decisions.* New York: Oxford University Press.

Coles, R. (1989). *The call of stories: teaching and the moral imagination*. Boston: Houghton Mifflin.

Crawford, J., Kippax, S., Onyx, J., & Gualt, U. (1992). *Emotion and gender: constructing meaning from memory*. Newbury Park, CA: Sage.

Davies, B. (2000). *A body of writing: 1990 - 1999*. Walnut Creek, CA: AltaMira Press.

Duerk, J. (1999). *Circle of stones: woman's journey to herself*. Philadelphia, PA: Innisfree Press.

Dunlop, R. (2002). Who will be the throat of these hours...if not I, if not you? *Educational Insights*. Retrieved February 23, 2004, from the World Wide Web: www.csci.educ.ubc.ca/publication/insights/v07n02/contextualexplorations/dunlop/.

Ellis, C. (1995). *Final negotiations: a story of love, loss and chronic illness*. Philadelphia, PA: Temple University Press.

Ellis, C., & Bochner, A. (2000). Autoethnography, personal narrative, reflexivity: researcher as subject. In N. K. Denzin & Y. S. Lincoln (Eds.), *Handbook of qualitative research* (pp. 733-768). Thousand Oaks, CA: Sage.

Ellsworth, E. (1989). Why doesn't this feel empowering? Working through the repressive myths of critical pedagogy. *Harvard Educational Review, 59*(3), 297-324.

Ellsworth, E. (1997). *Teaching positions: difference, pedagogy, and the power of address*. New York: Teachers College Press.

Freshwater, D. (2000). Crosscurrents: against cultural narration in nursing. *Journal of Advanced Nursing, 32*(2), 481-484.

Freshwater, D. (2006). Crosscurrents: against cultural narration in nursing. *Journal of Advanced Nursing, 32*(2), 481-484.

Gingras, J. (2004). Like cold water or a kiss: reflections on transformative teaching. In M. G. Smith, L. Peterat & M. L. de Zwart (Eds.), *Home economics now: transformative practice, ecology, and everyday life. A tribute to the scholarship of Eleanore Vaines.* (pp. 67-75). Vancouver, BC: Pacific Educational Press.

Gussow, J. D. (1999). Dietary guidelines for sustainability: twelve years later. *Journal of Nutrition Education, 31*(4), 194-200.

Harding, S. G. (1991). *Whose science? Whose knowledge? Thinking from women's lives.* Ithaca, NY: Cornell University Press.

Hejinian, L. (2000). *The language of inquiry.* Berkeley, CA: University of California Press.

Hieddeger, M. (1971). What are poets for? (A. Hofstadter, Trans.), *Poetry, language, thought.* (pp. 91-142). New York: Harper & Row Publishers.

hooks, b. (1994). *Teaching to transgress: education as the practice of freedom.* New York: Routledge.

hooks, b. (2000). *All about love: new visions.* New York: William Morrow.

hooks, b. (2003). *Teaching community: a pedagogy of hope.* New York: Routledge.

Jardine, D. (1998). Wild hearts, silent traces, and journeys of lament, *To dwell with a boundless heart: essays in curriculum theory, hermeneutics, and the ecological imagination* (pp. 135-144). New York: Peter Lang.

Johnston, R. J., Gregory, D., Pratt, G., & Watts, M. (Eds.). (2000). *The dictionary of human geography* (4th ed.). Malden, Massachusetts: Blackwell Publishers.

Lather, P. (1991). Deconstructing/deconstructive inquiry: the politics of knowing and being known. *Educational Theory, 41*(2), 153-173.

Launer, J. (2004). Reflective practice and clinical supervision: developing supervision skills. *Work Based Learning in Primary Care, 2*(3), 264-266.

Norman, R., Leggo, C. (1995). Living our gendered experiences: Composing narratives out of fears and tears. *English Quarterly, 27*(1-2), 15-21.

Levinson, N. (2001). The paradox of natality: teaching in the midst of belatedness. In M. Gordon (Ed.), *Hannah Arendt and education: renewing our common world.* (pp. 11-36). Boulder, Colo.: Westview Press.

Lorde, A. (1984). Poetry is not a luxury., *Sister/outsider.* (pp. 36-39). Freedom, CA: The Crossing Press.

Love, H. (2004). Dwelling in ambivalence. *The Women's Review of Books, 22*(2), 18-19.

Lupton, D. (1996). *Food, the body, and the self.* London; Thousand Oaks, CA: Sage.

Martin, C. (2002). *The scientist.* London: Capitol/EMI Records.

Mills, C. (2004). In P. J. Eakin (Ed.), *The ethics of life writing.* New York: Cornell University Press.

Norman, R. (1995). A dramatic conception of curriculum: artistic, emancipated and feminist possibilities through the emotional. *Educational Insights.* Retrieved May 30, 2005, from the World Wide Web: http://www.ccfi.educ.ubc.ca/publication/insights/archives/v03n01/norman.html.

Nussbaum, M. (1999). The professor of parody. *New Republic.*

Okri, B. (1997). *A way of being.* London: Phoenix House.

Orr, D. W. (1994). What is education for?, *Earth in mind: on education, environment, and the human prospect* (pp. 7-15). Washington, DC: Island Press.

Pearson, Q. M. (2001). A case in clinical supervision: a framework for putting theory into practice. *Journal of Mental Health Counseling, 23,* 174-183.

Pelias, R. J. (2004). *A methodology of the heart: evoking academic and daily life.* Walnut Creek, CA: AltaMira Press.

Pinar, W. F., Reynolds, W. M., Slattery, P., & Taubman, P. M. (2002). Understanding curriculum as poststructuralist, deconstructed, postmodern text, *Understanding curriculum: an introduction to the study of historical and contemporary curriculum discourses.* (pp. 450-514). New York: Peter Lang Publishing, Inc.

Richardson, L. (1992). The consequences of poetic representation: writing the other, rewriting the self. In C. Ellis & M. G. Flaherty (Eds.), *Investigating subjectivity: research on lived experience.* (pp. 125-137). Newbury Park, CA: Sage Publications.

Rukeyser, M. (1935). *Theory of flight.* New Haven: Yale University Press.

Rukeyser, M. (1996). *The life of poetry.* Ashfield, Massachusetts: Paris Press.

Sedgwick, E. (1990). *Epistemology of the closet.* Berkeley, CA: The University of California Press.

Sho-Mo and the Monkey Bunch. (2004). *Wee baby moon.* Toronto, ON: Tri-pop Records.

Smith, D. E. (1987). *The everyday world as problematic: a feminist sociology.* Toronto: University of Toronto Press.

Søndergaard, D. M. (2005). Academic desire trajectories: retooling the concepts of subject, desire, and biography. *European Journal of Women's Studies, 12*(3), 297-313.

Taubes, G. (2001). The soft science of dietary fat. *Science, 291*(5513), 2536-2545.

Travers, K. D. (1995). "Do you teach them how to budget?": Professional discourse in the construction of nutritional inequities. In D. Maurer & J. Sobal (Eds.), *Eating agendas: food and nutrition as social problems.* (pp. 213-240). New York: Aldine de Gruyter.

Wiesel, E. (1990). *Global education.* Paper presented at the Global Forum, Moscow.

Woolf, V. (1991). *A room of one's own.* New York: Harcourt Brace Jovanovich.